Medicare for Beginners 2024-2025 Edition Simplified Guide

Uncover Affordable Healthcare Secrets and Discover the Optimal Plan for You and Your Loved Ones Avoid Medicare mistakes with this Guide

TABLE OF CONTENTS:

INTRODU

Navigating the world of healthcare can be a daunting task, especially when it comes to understanding the intricacies of Medicare. This book aims to demystify the complex world of Medicare and provide you with the knowledge you need to make informed decisions about your healthcare.

In Chapter 1, we delve into the basics of Medicare, breaking down its different parts - Part A, Part B, Part C, and Part D - and explaining what each cover. This foundational knowledge will help you understand the rest of the book and the Medicare system as a whole.

Chapter 2 provides practical advice on reducing your Medicare expenses, while Chapter 3 covers the critical periods for enrollment and the penalties for late enrollment. In Chapter 4, we discuss the Medicare Star Ratings, a system that rates the quality of Medicare Advantage plans.

Chapter 5 outlines the qualifications for Medicare, providing a clear understanding of who is eligible for each part of Medicare. In Chapter 6, we discuss what living with Medicare looks like, providing practical advice for managing your healthcare under this system.

Chapter 7 outlines ten common mistakes people make with Medicare and how to avoid them, while Chapter 8 explains your rights as a

Medicare recipient. This chapter is crucial for understanding how to advocate for yourself within the Medicare system.

Finally, Chapter 9 provides a guide on how to buy Medicare insurance by yourself, outlining three different options and explaining the pros and cons of each.

The conclusion wraps up the book, summarizing the key points and providing final thoughts on navigating the Medicare system.

This book is designed to be a comprehensive guide to Medicare, providing you with the knowledge and tools you need to navigate this complex system with confidence. Whether you're new to Medicare or have been a recipient for years, this book will provide valuable insights and practical advice to help you make the most of your healthcare.

CHAPTER 1: WHAT IS MEDICARE?

The U.S. government funds the Medicare health insurance program, established in 1965 under Title XVIII of the Social Security Act. Its primary purpose is to offer healthcare coverage to U.S. citizens aged 65 and above, and certain disabled individuals under 65. The Centers for Medicare and Medicaid Services (CMS), a branch of the U.S. Department of Health and Human Services, administers Medicare. Eligible individuals can join the national program to obtain health insurance coverage, irrespective of their financial status or medical history.

The origins of Medicare can be traced back to the early 20th century when the U.S. contemplated a national health insurance program. However, substantial progress wasn't made until the mid-1960s. President Lyndon B. Johnson signed the legislation that established Medicare in 1965 as part of his Great Society domestic policy.

Medicare's various coverage levels provide specific services:

1. Medicare Part A (Hospital Insurance): Covers hospice care, inpatient hospital stays, skilled nursing facility care, and some home health services. Typically, there are no premiums for Part A if the individual or their spouse paid Medicare taxes during their working years.

2. Medicare Part B (Medical Insurance): Covers preventive care, outpatient therapy, doctor visits, and necessary medical supplies. This insurance requires a monthly income-based premium.

3. Medicare Part C (Medicare Advantage): Allows non-government insurance providers to offer Medicare-approved plans. These plans often provide additional benefits like prescription drug coverage and dental or vision care. Medicare Advantage programs may vary in cost and coverage requirements from traditional Medicare.

4. Medicare Part D (Prescription Drug Coverage): This standalone prescription drug coverage is provided by private insurance companies. It is available to all Medicare beneficiaries and assists with prescription medication costs. A monthly premium is required, and the specific medications covered are outlined in the plans' formularies.

When individuals first become eligible for Medicare, they have a specific timeframe to sign up for each component. If they miss this opportunity, they may face late enrollment penalties or have to wait until the next open enrollment period.

Medicare enrollees have two options for receiving medical care (Part C). Original Medicare allows beneficiaries to see any doctor or hospital that accepts Medicare, while Medicare Advantage plans typically have networks of doctors and hospitals.

Medicare is funded through payroll taxes, premiums from beneficiaries, and general government revenue. It plays a vital role in providing affordable healthcare coverage to millions of Americans, particularly the elderly and those with disabilities.

However, it's important to note that Medicare doesn't cover all medical expenses. Individuals are responsible for their own deductibles, copayments, and coinsurance. Some choose to supplement their coverage with additional commercial insurance, like Medigap policies, to help offset some of the out-of-pocket costs associated with Medicare.

Grasp the Scope of Medicare Coverage.

To make informed healthcare choices, beneficiaries need to grasp the extent of coverage that Medicare provides. To gain a comprehensive understanding of the benefits offered, we will delve into all the Medicare coverage alternatives in this discourse.

1. Medicare Part A: Comprehensive Hospital Insurance

Primarily designed to cover inpatient care, Medicare Part A exhibits several key features:

● Hospitalization: This plan encompasses inpatient hospital care, including essential stays, semi-private rooms, meals, basic nursing services, prescribed drugs, and vital medical supplies and equipment. It also extends to Intensive Care Units (ICUs), critical access hospitals, and hospital-based mental health services.

● Skilled Nursing Facilities (SNFs): Medicare Part A covers services rendered in SNFs, including nursing care, therapy, and post-hospitalization rehabilitation. However, two conditions must be satisfied: the SNF care must be related to a prior condition and the patient must have had a preceding hospital stay of at least three days.

- Home Health Care: A limited range of home health care services are covered, provided certain conditions are met.

- Hospice Care: For terminally ill patients, this plan covers pain medication, symptom management, and emotional support for both the patient and their family.

Despite its comprehensive coverage for hospital-related services, Medicare Part A has certain restrictions and costs to bear in mind:

- Beneficiaries are required to pay deductibles and coinsurance for hospital stays, and these amounts are subject to yearly changes. For instance, in 2023, the deductible for each benefit period is $1,576, and coinsurance charges begin to accumulate after a specified number of days.

- The coverage operates on benefit periods and has a duration limit. Once a new benefit period commences, the beneficiary must pay the deductible again.

- Long-term care in nursing homes or assisted living facilities is not covered. It only provides limited coverage for post-hospitalization skilled nursing care in a certified facility.

The eligibility criteria for Medicare Part A are as follows:

1. Age: Typically, Medicare Part A coverage is available to individuals aged 65 or older. They must have lived in the US for a minimum of five years and be US citizens or permanent residents.

2. Disability: Individuals under 65 who have been receiving Railroad Retirement Board (RRB) benefits may qualify.

3. End-Stage Renal Disease (ESRD): Individuals of any age with ESRD, such as chronic kidney disease requiring dialysis, are eligible.

4. Amyotrophic Lateral Sclerosis (ALS): These individuals are automatically eligible for coverage in the same month their disability benefits commence.

Although Medicare Part A offers numerous benefits, including covering hospital stays and skilled nursing care, it also has limitations due to deductibles, coinsurance, and time restrictions. Eligibility for Medicare Part A is primarily determined by age, disability, or specific health conditions. A thorough understanding of the scope, benefits, limitations, and eligibility requirements of Medicare Part A is crucial when planning for post-retirement healthcare or when dealing with particular health issues.

2. Medicare Part B: Comprehensive Medical Insurance

Medicare Part B provides extensive coverage for a broad array of crucial medical services and supplies, including outpatient care, durable medical equipment, physician consultations, and preventative services. In this discussion, we'll delve into its benefits, constraints, and prerequisites.

Benefits:

Medicare Part B offers a plethora of benefits to its enrollees. Key advantages include:

● Doctor and specialist appointments: This coverage encompasses all outpatient medical examinations, procedures, and consultations.

● Outpatient Treatments: It includes all diagnostic tests and ambulatory surgical procedures. Outpatient mental health therapies, including counseling and therapy sessions, are also covered.

- Preventive care, the cornerstone of Part B, includes a variety of screenings, immunizations, and counseling services aimed at early disease detection and prevention. Examples include heart check-ups, colonoscopies, flu vaccines, and mammograms.

- Medical equipment such as wheelchairs, walkers, oxygen equipment, and prosthetic devices are covered, subject to certain conditions and restrictions.

- Home health services: For those homebound and in need of specialized care.

- Ambulance Services: It covers both emergency and non-emergency ambulance services when other transportation methods are unsafe or unsuitable.

Limitations: Despite its comprehensive coverage, Medicare Part B has certain limitations and exclusions to be mindful of. Here are some notable constraints:

- Cost-sharing: Along with monthly premiums, annual deductibles, and coinsurance, Part B expects beneficiaries to contribute a coinsurance or copayment. These amounts may vary annually.

- Routine dental care, eyeglasses, hearing aids, cosmetic procedures, and most prescription drugs are not covered by this insurance. Some procedures may necessitate additional insurance or out-of-pocket costs.

- Coverage Gaps: Part B may not fully cover the cost of certain products or services. Beneficiaries are responsible for any additional costs, which might include extra charges if the provider declines the amount approved by Medicare.

- Prior Authorization: Under certain circumstances, Part B may necessitate prior authorization for specific services or treatments. This implies that Medicare approval must be obtained before the treatment is administered to ensure coverage.

Eligibility Criteria: The eligibility requirements for Medicare Part B include:

● Age: Applicants are generally required to be 65 or older. Exceptions are made for individuals below 65 with disabilities.

● Enrollment in Part A: To be eligible for Medicare Part B, which provides hospital insurance, one must first be enrolled in Medicare Part A.

● Residency: An individual must have been a US citizen for at least five years.

● Enrollment periods: Individuals can enroll during specific periods. The initial enrollment period is three months before and after turning 65. There are also general and special enrollment periods for certain situations.

● Premiums: Your income determines your monthly premium for Part B. While most beneficiaries pay the standard premium, those with higher incomes may be charged more.

Understanding the benefits, limitations, and eligibility criteria for Medicare Part B is crucial. This coverage plays a significant role in providing millions of Americans with access to essential medical treatments, outpatient care, and preventative screenings.

3. Medicare Part C: An Overview of Medicare Advantage

Medicare Advantage, also known as Medicare Part C, is a health insurance alternative offered by approved commercial insurance companies. It integrates the benefits of the first two Medicare coverages and often includes additional coverage for elements such as prescription drugs, dental, vision, and hearing needs. In this discussion, we will explore the advantages, limitations, and eligibility requirements of Medicare Part C.

Medicare Part C provides several benefits over traditional Medicare, including broader coverage options and potential cost savings. Some of its key benefits include:

● Comprehensive Coverage: It typically encompasses all services covered by the first two Medicare plans, including hospital stays, doctor visits, lab tests, and preventive care.

● Prescription Drug Coverage: Many Medicare Part C plans include coverage for prescription drugs, offering beneficiaries access to a wide variety of medications at potentially lower prices than standalone Part D plans.

● Additional Services: Unlike traditional Medicare, Medicare Part C often covers dental care, vision care (including eyeglasses), hearing aids, and wellness programs. These additional benefits can be particularly useful for individuals with specific health concerns.

• Coordinated Care: Medicare Advantage plans usually involve a network of medical professionals who coordinate patient care, potentially simplifying and streamlining healthcare delivery.

However, it's crucial to understand the limitations of Medicare Part C:

• Preferred Provider Networks: Most Medicare Advantage plans have a preferred provider network, which can limit healthcare options.

• Prior Authorization: Some Medicare Advantage plans may require prior authorization for beneficiaries to receive certain services, such as expensive diagnostic tests or surgeries. This could potentially delay care due to necessary additional documentation and approval processes.

• Regional Variation: The benefits of Medicare Advantage plans and their availability can vary by location. Some plans may only be accessible in specific regions, potentially limiting options for beneficiaries in certain areas.

• Annual Changes: Medicare Advantage plans can alter their provider networks and benefits annually. Beneficiaries should review plan updates and changes during the annual enrollment process to ensure their chosen plan continues to meet their healthcare needs.

The eligibility criteria for Medicare Part C include:

- Enrollment in the first two Medicare coverages.

- Residency: Beneficiaries must live within the coverage area of the plan. Service areas can vary depending on the location and the plan, so it's important to confirm that the plans are available in the beneficiary's area.

- Enrollment Periods: Individuals become eligible for Medicare Advantage at the same time they first become eligible for Medicare.

4. Medicare Part D: Coverage for Prescription Medications

Medicare Part D is a scheme designed to reduce personal expenditure by covering the cost of prescription drugs while also offering members a broad spectrum of medication options. It provides access to both branded and generic drugs, along with assistance in managing the cost of prescription medications. However, it does have notable limitations, including a coverage gap and certain eligibility requirements. Those considering enrolling in Medicare Part D should thoroughly assess their needs, compare various plans, and take into account any existing coverage to ensure it aligns with their unique requirements.

CHAPTER 2: REDUCING YOUR MEDICARE EXPENSES

Addressing the issue of escalating Medicare costs necessitates a comprehensive approach that takes into account a multitude of factors. Here are a few potential strategies that could help in curtailing Medicare expenses:

- Emphasizing Preventive Care: Encouraging preventive care and wellness programs can facilitate the early detection of health problems, thereby averting the need for costlier treatments later. Regular health checks, screenings, and vaccinations can mitigate the incidence and severity of chronic illnesses, consequently lessening their financial impact on Medicare.

- Integrated Care Coordination: Enhancing care coordination and integration among different healthcare providers can eliminate duplicative services and reduce unnecessary hospital readmissions. The costs to Medicare due to disjointed and uncoordinated care can be mitigated by improving communication and information sharing among healthcare professionals, leading to more effective and efficient patient care.

- Chronic Disease Management: Effective management of chronic conditions such as diabetes, hypertension, and heart disease can significantly reduce Medicare costs. By investing in programs that provide information, self-management tools, and access to affordable medication, we can help individuals better manage their conditions, leading to fewer complications and hospitalizations.

• Value-Based Care: Shifting from a volume-based to a value-based payment model, where clinicians are compensated based on patient satisfaction and outcomes rather than the number of services provided, can encourage cost-effective practices and curtail Medicare expenses.

• Negotiating Drug Prices: Medicare should be empowered to negotiate drug prices directly with pharmaceutical companies, which could significantly lower the cost of prescription drugs. Leveraging the government's purchasing power could result in considerable savings for both Medicare beneficiaries and the program itself.

• Fraud and Waste Prevention: Implementing robust anti-fraud measures and enhancing oversight can help detect and prevent Medicare fraud and abuse. By using data analytics to identify suspicious billing patterns and strengthening auditing systems, we can safeguard Medicare funds and reduce unnecessary expenditure.

• Health Information Technology (HIT): The widespread and efficient use of HIT can boost productivity, reduce medical errors, and cut administrative costs. By streamlining electronic health records (EHRs), promoting interoperability among various systems, and encouraging telemedicine, we can enhance care coordination, reduce unnecessary tests, and improve patient outcomes, all while saving costs.

● End-of-Life Care: Facilitating open discussions about end-of-life care preferences can help patients make informed decisions and avoid unnecessary and costly interventions. By expanding access to palliative care and hospice services, we can improve patients' quality of life and reduce Medicare costs associated with aggressive, ineffective treatments.

● Transition Care Coordination: Enhancing care coordination during transitions, such as from hospitals to nursing homes or home care, can minimize the risk of adverse outcomes and hospital readmissions. Optimal patient outcomes and lower healthcare costs can be achieved through funding care transition programs, medication reconciliation, and post-discharge follow-up.

● Health Literacy: Improving health literacy empowers Medicare beneficiaries to make informed decisions, manage their health better, and utilize the healthcare system more efficiently. Providing clear and accessible educational resources can lead to improved health outcomes and fewer costly medical procedures.

Reducing Medicare costs while maintaining the quality of care for beneficiaries requires careful planning, implementation, and evaluation. Strategies involving multiple approaches may need to be tailored based on the local healthcare landscape and the specific needs of the Medicare population.

CHAPTER 3: ENROLLMENT AND ELECTION PERIODS, LATE ENROLLMENT PENALTIES

If you've conducted any online research, discussed Medicare with acquaintances, or perused the government-provided Medicare and You guide, you've likely encountered the term "enrollment penalties". These are financial penalties that you will incur for the remainder of your life if you fail to timely enroll in Medicare Part B and Medicare Part D. This is indeed accurate. However, in this segment, I'll clarify how these penalties function and how you can sidestep them.

To understand this, we first need to discuss Election Periods. These periods specify when you can enroll in Medicare and Medicare insurance plans, and they cover a wide range of situations.

Each Election Period has an associated acronym to cover virtually every conceivable situation. The terms "enrollment" and "election" are frequently used interchangeably, which can lead to confusion. To complicate things further, there are numerous such acronyms, over thirty by my reckoning.

Just been released from prison? Welcome back! There's a code for that. Is your Medicare Advantage plan withdrawing from your service area? There's a code for that too. Unable to enroll in your preferred insurance plan due to a FEMA-declared weather-related emergency or disaster? Yes, there's a code for that as well.

Don't fret, you don't need to memorize all of them, or even the majority of them, and you certainly don't need to remember the acronyms. You simply need to be aware of their existence and that they can be utilized.

Insurance company phone representatives and proficient independent Medicare insurance agents are well-versed in these rules. It's part of their job. Therefore, if you have a reliable agent, don't hesitate to request their guidance on this matter, but avoid doing so a week before your 65th birthday. Although technically possible, I would recommend planning well in advance if feasible. Nothing ever goes perfectly according to plan when rushed. Try to do it in the year leading up to your birthday or when you become eligible for Medicare, especially if you have a unique situation. Typical scenarios include (a) still working past sixty-five, (b) having a younger spouse or partner on your employer-sponsored group health insurance, (c) being disabled but not yet having completed your twenty-four months of Social Security Disability to qualify for Medicare, or spending part of the year overseas, moving, etc.

There are four Election Periods that I believe you should be familiar with, which are detailed in the following pages. This doesn't mean you need to memorize them. As previously stated, just be generally aware of what they are:

1. Initial Enrollment Period (IEP)

The Initial Enrollment Period (IEP) for Medicare Part A and Part B is a seven-month window that begins three months before your 65th birthday. This period includes your birth month and extends for another three months after. During this time, you can register for Original Medicare Parts A and B and choose from three different coverage options.

For many, Medicare coverage is automatically activated during this period, requiring no action on their part other than checking their mail. This includes:

a. Individuals turning 65 who are already beneficiaries of Social Security or the Railroad Retirement Board.

b. Individuals under 65 with disabilities who have been receiving disability benefits for 24 months.

c. Individuals diagnosed with ALS (Amyotrophic Lateral Sclerosis) who receive coverage the month their Social Security benefits commence.

However, there are cases where proactive Medicare registration is required:

a. Individuals nearing 65 who are not receiving Social Security benefits.

b. Residents of Puerto Rico, who must separately register for Part B.

To illustrate the process, consider Jane, who turns 65 on June 22. If Jane registers for Medicare anytime in March, April, or May, her coverage begins June 1. If she registers in June, coverage begins July 1. If she registers in July or August, coverage begins two and three months later, respectively. If Jane fails to register for Part B during this period, she will face the Part B Late Enrollment Penalty, which will be added to her Part B premium for life.

As the age for full Social Security benefits increases to 67, more people are eligible for Medicare at 65 but choose to delay Social Security until after 65.

My advice? If you fall into this category and need to actively register, do so as early as possible before turning 65, ideally three months prior. Do not terminate your existing insurance coverage until you receive written confirmation of your Medicare coverage dates. Avoid any coverage gaps by planning and acting early. If you're uninsured, register for Medicare as soon as you're eligible.

Moreover, the earlier your Medicare coverage begins, the sooner you can register for a Medicare Part D Prescription Drug Plan, Medicare Advantage plan, or Medicare Supplement plan. If you register early, these coverages will be effective immediately when your Medicare Parts A and B are activated.

I'm one of the folks that need to sign up. How do I do it?

If you wish to register, navigate to the appropriate section on the Social Security website. It's advisable to do this as promptly as possible, as the processing period can be lengthy, similar to the Department of Motor Vehicles (DMV). Here are your options:

- Online registration. The link and instructions can be found on the website. Visit https://secure.ssa.gov/iClaim/rib. This is the most efficient and convenient method in my view.

- Personal visit to your local Social Security office. The locations of these offices can also be located online.

- Telephone registration with Social Security. Be prepared for potentially long waiting times, possibly exceeding an hour. The contact number is 1-800-772-1213.

Social Security provides a checklist of the information required for Medicare registration. It's worth noting that you'll likely automatically receive Medicare Part A and B.

MEDICARE PART B LATE ENROLLMENT PENALTY

Eligibility for Medicare Part B carries a penalty for late enrollment if you actively decide against it. Not only will you lack the coverage detailed earlier, but should you eventually decide to enroll, you'll face a lifelong penalty. This penalty amounts to an additional 10% increase on the Part B premium for each year you could have had Part B but chose not to.

However, if you delay enrollment in Part B due to continued employment past the age of sixty-five and receive health insurance from your employer, you won't face a penalty for late enrollment. Once you retire and wish to enroll in Medicare Part B, you can do so then. The penalty only applies if you could and should have enrolled in Medicare Part B but decided against it. If you declined Medicare Part B without any alternative insurance and later wished to enroll, you could do so during the General Enrollment Period (beginning on January 1 each year), but you would incur the lifelong premium penalty.

PART D LATE ENROLLMENT PENALTY

Medicare Part D also carries a late enrollment penalty. According to Medicare, this penalty is a permanent addition to your Medicare drug coverage (Medicare Part D) premium. You may incur a late enrollment penalty if, following your Initial Enrollment Period, there is a continuous sixty-three-day period or more when you lack Medicare drug coverage or other credible prescription drug coverage. This penalty generally applies for as long as you have Medicare drug coverage.

If you fail to enroll in Medicare Part D when first eligible, either through a Medicare Part D Prescription Drug plan or a Medicare Advantage plan, you will face a financial penalty if you decide to enroll later. It's advisable to enroll as soon as you're eligible, even if you don't currently need it. In fact, it's more than advisable. If you don't, the late enrollment financial penalty (higher premiums) will affect you for the rest of your life. Even if you don't currently take any prescriptions, chances are you will at some point. It's best to choose the least expensive Medicare Part D plan when you're eligible to avoid the late enrollment penalty. You can change your Part D Prescription Drug Plan and Medicare Advantage plan once per year under normal circumstances during the AEP. This means that even if you initially choose the cheapest plan because you're not currently taking any prescriptions, you can change it annually if your status changes.

Don't worry, just like Medicare Part B, you won't be penalized for not purchasing it if you're working past the age of sixty-five and have prescription drug coverage through your employer or elsewhere, but you'll have to demonstrate it was "creditable" coverage to Medicare (as good as or better than Medicare Part D) when you do eventually sign up.

So, you should enroll in Medicare Part B and obtain Medicare Part D coverage, either through a stand-alone Medicare Part D Prescription Drug Plan or a MAPD plan when you turn sixty-five. Right? Well, yes. Unless...

EXTENDING EMPLOYMENT BEYOND THE STANDARD RETIREMENT AGE

Approximately 40% of individuals continue to work beyond the conventional retirement age of sixty-five. However, by the age of seventy, a majority have ceased full-time employment. If you're among those still working, you can delay enrollment (and payment) for Medicare Part B without incurring penalties when you eventually decide to apply. Here are some considerations:

If you're still employed by a company with more than twenty employees and receive health insurance benefits through your employer, you may wish to maintain this arrangement. Perhaps your employer covers all your premiums, or maybe your spouse or partner isn't yet eligible for Medicare and you're providing their insurance. In such scenarios, you can opt for Part A and postpone enrollment in Part

B. If this situation applies to you, you won't face a Part B penalty when you eventually retire and enroll, provided you have "creditable coverage."

If you're employed by a company with fewer than twenty employees, you'll need to enroll in Medicare Parts A and B when you're eligible. The reasons behind this are not relevant to you as a consumer. It's generally advisable to relinquish your employer plan at this point, even while still employed, as employer-sponsored health insurance is typically more costly than Medicare Parts A and B and any additional Medicare insurance plans you might add.

What if you're providing health insurance for your spouse or partner through your employer, and they're not yet eligible for Medicare?

You'll need to make a decision. You can continue to work and provide employer-based health insurance until your spouse or partner is eligible for Medicare, or you can stop working, take Medicare Parts A and B, and purchase an Affordable Care Act Plan for your spouse or partner. You can explore your Affordable Care Act Plan options at http://www.healthcare.gov.

In most cases, it will be more cost-effective for you to continue working, relinquish your employer coverage, enroll in Medicare Parts A and B, and sign up for additional Medicare insurance on top of Original Medicare (Medicare Part D Prescription Drug Plan, a Medicare Advantage plan, or a Medicare Supplement plan).

It's important to note that to Medicare, Creditable Coverage does not include COBRA coverage, certain retiree health plans, or VA coverage. Don't presume you have creditable coverage and delay signing up for Part B. Complete the application promptly.

If you have an Affordable Care Act plan, you can technically maintain it while on Medicare, but it's unlikely to be financially beneficial. This is because you won't receive any premium tax credits or other cost savings, and you'll pay the full price. If you have an ACA plan, there's a comprehensive overview and checklist available online. However, it's generally not advantageous for most individuals to keep an ACA plan once they have Medicare.

Some employers now permit employees to enroll in Medicare while still covering family members, which can be more cost-effective for the employer. There are always exceptions and unique arrangements, so it's best to consult your HR department.

Remember, if you delay enrollment in Part B or Part D, Medicare will require proof of coverage when you eventually sign up. Don't discard your paperwork. Your HR department will need to provide a CMS-L564E form confirming you had group health plan coverage.

When your employer-based group coverage ends, you will have eight months to enroll in Medicare Part B, regardless of your age. Failure to do so within eight months will result in a penalty.

However, when you eventually relinquish your employer coverage, you only have sixty-three days to enroll in Medicare Part D prescription drug benefits, either through a Medicare Advantage plan or a standalone Medicare Part D Prescription Drug Plan. It's crucial to enroll in Parts D and B within the first sixty days to ensure coverage.

If you continue to work past the age of 65 and eventually choose to enroll in Medicare Parts B and D, be prepared for a lengthy and potentially complicated process. Deferred off-cycle Medicare elections can confuse Social Security Administration staff, and issues such as long wait times on Medicare and Social Security phone lines, lack of timely appointment availability at the Social Security Administration, and federal agency staffing problems are common. Start early and document everything, including dates, times, names, and notes.

1.5 Initial Coverage Election Period (ICEP)

If for any reason you choose to postpone your enrollment in Medicare Part B, when you eventually decide to enroll, your election period code will likely be the Initial Coverage Election Period or ICEP. I highly recommend consulting a Medicare insurance agent during this decision-making process and throughout the entire procedure. They should be able to guide you effectively to avoid missing any deadlines.

If you've comprehended the information above and decided to postpone Part B for some time, here's how you can do it:

For most individuals, upon turning sixty-five, you automatically receive Medicare Part A. If you're drawing Social Security, you also automatically receive Medicare Part B. However, if you wish to defer Medicare Part B, there is a form included in the packet you receive before turning sixty-five. Completing this form will allow you to postpone your Medicare Part B enrollment until a later date.

If you wish to temporarily opt out of Part B until a later date, here's the procedure:

If your Medicare coverage hasn't begun yet, there are two methods to opt out of Part B:

• If you were automatically enrolled in both Part A and Part B and received a Medicare card, follow the instructions provided with the card and return it. If you retain the card, you'll keep Part B and will be required to pay Part B premiums.

• If you enrolled in Medicare via Social Security, you should contact them. If your Medicare coverage has already started and you wish to opt out of Part B, reach out to Social Security for instructions on how to submit a signed request. Your coverage will cease on the first day of the month following the receipt of your request by Social Security.

The contact number for Social Security is 800-772-1213. If you prefer, you can also visit a Social Security office.

2. Annual Election Period (AEP)

The Annual Election Period (AEP) commences each year on October 15 and concludes on December 7. During this interval, you may notice an influx of advertisements and commercials from insurance companies on your mailbox, web browsers, and television screens. These companies are aiming to persuade you to purchase or switch your Medicare Advantage or Medicare Part D Prescription Drug Plans.

This period provides the opportunity to modify your Medicare Advantage plan or your Medicare Part D Prescription Drug Plan if desired. For example, during the AEP, it is possible to transition from Original Medicare to Medicare Advantage, or the reverse. Additionally, you may choose to switch from one Medicare Advantage plan to another that better aligns with your requirements or financial situation.

Similarly, you have the option to switch from one Medicare Part D Prescription Drug Plan to another, or to join or leave a Medicare Part D plan entirely. Provided these changes are made during the AEP, your new coverage will commence on January 1 of the following year, and your previous plan will be immediately discontinued, ensuring no gap in coverage.

It's important to note that these changes do not apply to Medicare Supplement (Medigap) insurance, which will be discussed later in the book. This period is solely for altering Medicare Advantage Plans and Medicare Part D Prescription Drug Plans.

If no changes are made during this period, your current plan will automatically continue into the next year.

Many writers and journalists erroneously refer to the AEP as "Open Enrollment" or "Annual Open Enrollment". This is incorrect; it is the Annual Election Period. This misnomer is a pet peeve of mine, and as this is my book, I feel compelled to correct it for my fellow writers and readers. It's crucial to distinguish between the two separate periods, as conflating them can be misleading and factually incorrect. There is an Annual Election Period and an...

3. Open Enrollment Period (OEP)

While the Annual Election Period (AEP) concludes annually on December 7th, it doesn't mean you're entirely out of options if you wish to modify your coverage after this date. With the AEP coinciding with the holiday season, it's understandable that some may overlook it. However, the Medicare Open Enrollment Period (OEP) offers another opportunity to adjust your Medicare coverage without penalties or waiting for the next AEP. If no changes are made, your current plan will automatically continue for the forthcoming year.

Also known as the Medicare Advantage Open Enrollment Period (MAOEP), the OEP runs from January 1st to March 31st each year. This period allows you to make adjustments if you're dissatisfied with your current plan or if circumstances have changed since the previous year. For instance, you may have overlooked the plan changes mailed to you by your insurance company in September and were caught off guard by an increased copay. Or perhaps your doctor's copay has risen, or they are no longer within your network. The OEP is the ideal time to consider alterations.

During the OEP, you have the option to:

- Transition to a different Medicare Advantage plan.

- Abandon your Medicare Advantage plan and revert to Original Medicare, Parts A and B. This allows you to sign up for a stand-alone Medicare Part D Prescription Drug Plan if you return to Original Medicare.

- Abandon your stand-alone Medicare Part D Prescription Drug Plan, although there are few reasons to do so.

However, during the OEP, you cannot:

- Switch from Original Medicare to a Medicare Advantage plan.

- Switch from one stand-alone Medicare Part D Prescription Drug Plan to another.

If you opt to abandon your Medicare Advantage plan and purchase a Medicare Part D Prescription Drug plan during the OEP, you'll be removed from your Medicare Advantage plan and default back to Original Medicare A and B for your medical insurance coverage. This might be an option if you're dissatisfied with your Medicare Advantage plan and wish to discard it. Consequently, you may also need or want to purchase a Medicare Supplement insurance plan at that time. However, if that's your intention, proceed with caution.

Medicare Supplement plans, unlike Original Medicare Parts A and B, Medicare Part D, or Medicare Part C (Medicare Advantage plans), can deny you coverage based on your health. A Medicare Supplement policy is a separate policy from Original Medicare Parts A and B and is offered by Medicare Supplement insurance companies. These companies can deny you coverage or, at minimum, accept you but charge a higher premium. If you're denied coverage for a Medicare Supplement plan, you'll only have Original Medicare Parts A and B and a Medicare Part D Prescription Drug plan to rely on, until the AEP (October 15-December 7th), when you can enroll in a Medicare Advantage plan once again. My advice is to apply and receive your acceptance or denial from the Medicare Supplement insurance company before you apply for a Medicare Part D Prescription Drug Plan and drop your Medicare Advantage plan.

In short, there's a very limited window to purchase a Medicare Supplement plan without answering medical questions, and the Medicare Supplement insurance company must accept your enrollment. Medicare Supplement plans have very strict timeframes within which you can apply for coverage and not be subject to medical underwriting.

If you're already on a Medicare Supplement, ensure you understand what you're doing. Many people use a Medicare Supplement for a few years then move to a Medicare Advantage plan. Some people move from one Medicare Supplement plan to another to get a cheaper rate. Whatever you do, don't drop a Medicare supplement plan before you get confirmation on your next insurance policy!

If you cancel a Medicare Supplement plan, it'll be challenging to get back onto it. If you drop your Medicare Advantage plan and revert to Original Medicare Parts A and B and a Medicare Part D Prescription Drug Plan, do not automatically assume you'll be able to buy a

Medicare Supplement plan. This is unlike Medicare Part D Prescription Drug Plans or Medicare Part C Medicare Advantage plans. Again, those types of plans must accept you with no medical underwriting.

If you leave a Medicare Advantage plan during the OEP, your current Medicare Advantage coverage will remain in force until the end of the current month. Your new coverage will then take effect on the first day of the following month. Please note, you can only make a change one time during the OEP. Once you have made a change to your Medicare coverage using your OEP, that's it for the year. You may not go back in during this same time frame and make more changes.

Here's an example of what you can't do during the OEP. Let's say you move from a Medicare Advantage plan back to Original Medicare on February 1st and pick up a Medicare Part D Prescription Drug Plan to cover your prescription drugs. That's it for the year. You're out of your OEP choices. Even if you change your mind, you cannot change your plan again on March 1 of the same year and go back into a Medicare Advantage plan. In that scenario, you'd have to wait until the AEP rolls around between October 15 and December 7.

In conclusion, make sure you have a valid reason and fully understand the benefits of your new plan, as well as what you may be sacrificing, before switching plans. The basic rule is this: don't drop Medicare Advantage in favor of a Medicare Supplement plus a Medicare Part D Prescription Drug Plan before you get accepted to enroll in a Medicare Supplement plan, if that's what you're planning to do. If you're okay with moving away from a Medicare Advantage plan and going back to Original Medicare plus a Medicare Part D Prescription Drug Plan, you can do that during the OEP. If you want to change from your current

Medicare Advantage plan and choose another one, you can do so—one time—during the OEP.

4. Special Enrollment Periods (SEP)

In essence, a Special Enrollment Period (SEP) allows you to alter your Medicare Advantage plan or Medicare prescription drug plan coverage outside of the standard enrollment periods.

There are over twenty-five different types of SEPs. If you believe you qualify for one or might be eligible, a knowledgeable independent Medicare insurance agent can be of great assistance. Alternatively, you could reach out to a Medicare insurance company for guidance. Even though the representatives may need to refer to their records to provide accurate information, they should be able to assist you. Medicare insurance agents may not remember all the SEPs, but they know where to find the information and how to apply it when necessary. If you encounter an unexpected event or special circumstance outside of the Initial Enrollment Period (IEP), Annual Enrollment Period (AEP), and Open Enrollment Period (OEP), an agent can be very helpful.

Here are a few commonly utilized SEPs:

MEDICARE ADVANTAGE "TRIAL PERIOD" SPECIAL ENROLLMENT PERIOD

This SEP is for individuals enrolling in a Medicare Advantage plan for the first time. They are given a "trial period" (up to twelve months) to evaluate the plan. If you are dissatisfied with the Medicare Advantage plan, this SEP allows you to revert to Original Medicare. You are also granted a "guaranteed issue right" to buy a Medicare supplement plan without undergoing any underwriting. This right is valid for sixty-three days post-disenrollment from the Medicare Advantage plan, hence timing and planning are crucial.

RELOCATION SEP

This SEP is applicable when you permanently relocate while on Medicare, enabling you to change your Medicare Advantage or Medicare Part D Prescription Drug Plan. If you move out of your current county or state, you are likely to move out of the service area of your insurance company. In such cases, you can enroll in a new Medicare Advantage plan or Medicare Part D Prescription Drug Plan, as per your needs.

SEP FOR INSTITUTIONALIZED INDIVIDUALS

This SEP is designed for individuals residing in nursing homes or other long-term care facilities. It allows you to enroll in or switch Medicare Advantage plans or Medicare Part D Prescription Drug Plan when you move into, live in, or are discharged from certain long-term care facilities. If you qualify, you can join a Medicare Advantage plan or Medicare Part D Prescription Drug Plan, switch to a different Medicare Advantage plan, or disenroll from Medicare Advantage and return to Original Medicare.

SEP FOR PEOPLE WITH LIMITED INCOME

Several SEPs are available for individuals with limited income, based on eligibility for various special "financial help" programs offered by states and the federal government. Generally, if you earn more than approximately $18,000 as an individual or less than $30,000 as a couple per year, you likely won't qualify.

To conclude, the expertise and guidance of a proficient Medicare insurance agent can be invaluable. Navigating the complexities of the various enrollment periods can be daunting, and you certainly don't want to miss crucial deadlines due to misunderstanding. Therefore, seeking professional help is highly recommended.

CHAPTER 4: MEDICARE STAR RATINGS

In today's world, ratings are ubiquitous. They can be found on platforms like Consumer Reports, Google, JD Power, Morningstar, Yelp, and numerous other businesses and sectors. We have been conditioned to make nearly all our purchases based on a five-star rating system, where five signifies excellence and one indicates poor quality.

Consider purchasing a Bluetooth speaker on Amazon. Upon entering "Bluetooth speaker" in the search bar, you're greeted with hundreds of options. To narrow down your choices, you likely first consider the price, and then the star rating. These ratings are provided by customers who have previously purchased and used the product, giving you a sense of confidence in your potential purchase.

This five-star rating system is also applicable to Medicare, specifically for Medicare Advantage and Medicare Part D Prescription Drug Plans. The Medicare Star rating system ranges from one to five, with five being the highest quality of service and one being the lowest.

Medicare Advantage plans are evaluated in five categories: maintaining health through screenings, tests, and vaccines; managing chronic conditions; plan responsiveness and care; member complaints and issues with services; and customer service. Medicare Part D Prescription Drug Plans are assessed in four categories: customer service, member complaints and issues with services, member experience with the plan, and drug pricing and patient safety.

Typically, the highest-rated Medicare Advantage plans are those that are highly integrated and strictly follow a "staff model" HMO plan. These plans, which often have small networks associated with a specific hospital or provider system, can control the customer experience from the moment they enter the doctor's office to their discharge from the hospital. This integrated approach often results in high customer satisfaction scores.

When a Medicare insurance company achieves a five-star rating, it receives financial bonuses from Medicare. While some of this money is retained by the company, most is used to enhance insurance benefits or reduce premiums. Additionally, five-star plans are granted a Special Enrollment Period (SEP), allowing them to enroll Medicare consumers outside of the standard AEP and OEP windows.

For 2022, only seventy-four out of over 3,800 plans measured achieved five stars. These top-rated plans include not only large, well-known companies, but also smaller, state-based or regional Medicare insurance companies. This demonstrates that even companies with smaller plans and less marketing budget can deliver high-quality Medicare insurance products on par with larger national Medicare insurance companies.

"UNRATED DUE TO NEWNESS"

Occasionally, when perusing star ratings, you may encounter Medicare Advantage plans and Medicare Part D Prescription Drug Plans that lack a star rating, instead displaying the message, "Unrated Due to Newness."

Why would a plan be labeled as such? The reason is that it's either being launched for the first time or is less than a year old. Consequently, Medicare lacks sufficient data to evaluate the plan. This doesn't imply that the Medicare insurance company that developed the plan is new; it merely indicates that this specific plan is new. Typically, "Unrated Due to Newness" is assigned a default star rating of three-and-a-half by Medicare, but this is not usually visible on Medicare.gov or the Medicare insurance company websites. This is merely the default rating these plans receive behind the scenes for their inaugural year.

Medicare Star Rating Process—How Much Weight Should You Give to the Star Ratings?

Firstly, the star ratings for plans displayed on Medicare.gov and in plan documents for Medicare insurance companies are at least a year outdated. This is due to the misalignment between the measurement periods and the deployment of Medicare Advantage and Medicare Part D Prescription Drug Plans. The delay can extend up to three years in some cases.

Secondly, Medicare modifies the criteria for scoring health plans annually. Consider this; over sixty-seven million people are enrolled in Medicare. Is it feasible to evaluate plan ratings nationwide using a single method? Can these ratings be neatly categorized into a five-star grading system? The clear answer is no, and policy experts and insurance companies subtly (and sometimes openly) communicate this to Medicare. Variations in location, access to medical facilities and physicians, income, and even perceptions of health, mean the results are questionable and flawed.

Another issue is the disparity between the Medicare star rating system and those of Amazon, Google, Yelp, and others; the star ratings are not primarily based on direct consumer feedback. Instead, they're derived from how Medicare and the federal government assess the Medicare insurance company plans, with a small portion of direct consumer feedback included. Medicare Advantage plans are evaluated on over forty quality and performance metrics, and Medicare Part D Prescription Drug Plans on up to fourteen.

Like most efforts to condense extensive information into a compact rating system for public convenience, it's unclear how it impacts the quality of your health insurance plan due to the plethora of data points Medicare monitors that don't apply uniformly to everyone on the same Medicare insurance plan. While consumer feedback does play a role, the majority of the rating methodology is based on medical and prescription drug data.

However, in my view, some of the questions posed are quite baffling. Here are a few that I find particularly perplexing:

• "In the past six months, how frequently did your health plan's customer service provide the information or assistance you required?" Possible responses include Never, Sometimes, Usually, Always.

What if you didn't need to contact customer service in the past six months? If you didn't, would you respond with "never"? "Never," by the way, counts as a negative score.

What if you can't recall what you did six months ago? (I, for one, couldn't even estimate the last time I dialed a customer service number.)

- "In the past six months, how frequently did your health plan's customer service treat you with courtesy and respect?" Possible responses include Never, Sometimes, Usually, Always.

Your interpretation of courtesy or respect might differ from mine, and both of ours might differ from our neighbors'. Is this a fair method for evaluating Medicare insurance companies?

- "Have you received a flu shot since July 1?"

Evidently, Medicare prefers a positive response (hence the question). What if I don't want a flu shot? What if it makes me feel unwell? What if I have a phobia of needles? If the response is negative, it's counted as a mark against the Medicare insurance company. Is this fair?

- "In the past six months, how often were you seen by the person you came to see within fifteen minutes of your appointment time?" Possible responses include Never, Sometimes, Usually, Always.

Have you ever visited the Emergency Room? Have you ever waited in your doctor's waiting room? Have you ever waited more than fifteen minutes? And if you had to wait, what could your health insurance company do about it? The answer is clear: nothing. Regardless, a negative response is a strike against the Medicare insurance plan.

OPT FOR PLANS RATED THREE-AND-A-HALF STARS OR ABOVE

If you remain inactive or refrain from making any changes, you will automatically continue with your current plan for the subsequent year.

Here's my suggestion; the star rating of a plan should be a crucial factor in your Medicare insurance coverage decision. I strongly recommend that you disregard any Medicare Advantage or Part D Prescription Drug Plan with a rating less than three-and-a-half stars. Nonetheless, the disparity between three and three-and-a-half or between three-and-a-half and four is not statistically significant. You are unlikely to notice the difference. In my view, Medicare Star ratings should not eclipse other factors such as premium, network, MOOP (Maximum-out-of-Pocket, discussed in the following chapter), or your prescription drug coverage.

If you remain inactive or refrain from making any changes, you will automatically continue with your current plan for the subsequent year.

However, star ratings are crucial to you because, generally, if your plan is rated three stars or below, it implies that you'll likely pay more for your policy, or your benefits won't be as comprehensive as those in plans rated four stars or above. This is because Medicare insurance companies receive bonuses and rebates from the federal government for higher star ratings. When they receive this bonus money, they are obliged to use a substantial portion of it to enhance the insurance benefits or reduce the monthly premiums for the Medicare insurance plan. Therefore, if you have a four-star rated plan, chances are you have superior benefits compared to a two-star rated plan.

This is another reason why I advise you to consider only Medicare insurance plans rated three-and-a-half stars or above. A low star rating is generally considered to be two-and-a-half or below. If a plan consistently scores at two-and-a-half stars or below, Medicare will add a "low performing plan" indicator on its own website. This symbol, an upside-down triangle with an exclamation point, often restricts enrollment from the Medicare website. Indeed, individuals enrolled in plans that receive this "low performing plan" status receive letters from Medicare notifying them of the company's performance. This is unfavorable for both the insurance company and the plan members!

Do star ratings truly matter? Absolutely. They are significant because they provide a comprehensive indication of the quality and customer experience of a given Medicare Advantage plan or Medicare Part D Prescription Drug Plan. Is there a considerable difference between a three-star plan and a four-star plan from the consumer's perspective or experience? Probably not. There are certainly flaws, and the regulations that insurance companies must comply with change annually. The real benefit to you, the consumer, is that higher-performing plans receive more funding from the federal government per person enrolled. Most of this additional funding must be reinvested into benefits or reduced insurance policy premiums, which, in the long run, is advantageous for you and your finances.

CHAPTER 5: QUALIFYING FOR MEDICARE

In order to be eligible for Medicare, certain specific criteria must be met. In the following discourse, we will delve into the prerequisites necessary for qualifying for the different aspects of Medicare coverage.

a. Medicare Part A: Hospital Coverage

To qualify for Medicare Part A, which covers hospital insurance, you must meet certain eligibility criteria. These include:

1. Age: Medicare Part A is generally available to individuals aged 65 and above. However, exceptions are made for those with specific disabilities or end-stage renal disease.

2. Citizenship or Legal Residency: Eligibility for Medicare Part A requires you to be a U.S. citizen or a legal resident who has resided in the United States continuously for a minimum of five years. Exceptions may be made for noncitizens who haven't met the five-year requirement but meet other specific conditions.

3. Eligibility through a Spouse's Work Record: If you haven't met the age requirement or haven't worked long enough to qualify for Medicare Part A based on your own work history, you may still be eligible if your spouse has worked and paid Medicare taxes for at least 10 years (equivalent to 40 quarters). In such cases, you can qualify for premium-free Medicare Part A based on your spouse's work record.

Remember, if you're receiving Social Security or Railroad Retirement Board payments when you turn 65, you'll be automatically enrolled in Medicare Part A, requiring no further action on your part.

b. Medicare Part B: Medical Coverage

To qualify for Medicare Part B, one must meet specific criteria set forth by the United States government. The following are the primary considerations:

● Age Criterion: Medicare Part B is automatically available to individuals 65 years old or above. Eligibility begins in the month of your 65th birthday. However, if you were born on the first day of the month, your coverage commences the preceding month.

● Disability: If you're under 65 and have been receiving Social Security Disability Insurance (SSDI) or specific Railroad Retirement Board disability benefits for 24 months, you automatically qualify for Medicare Part B.

● End-Stage Renal Disease (ESRD): Regardless of age, individuals with ESRD, including those needing regular dialysis or a kidney transplant, can access Medicare Part B. The coverage typically commences after a waiting period, usually three months.

● Amyotrophic Lateral Sclerosis (ALS): Those diagnosed with ALS, also known as Lou Gehrig's disease, automatically qualify for Medicare Part B in the month their disability benefits begin, with no waiting period.

- Enrollment in Medicare Part A: To qualify for Medicare Part B, you must be enrolled in Medicare Part A, which covers hospital services. Most people are automatically enrolled in Part A when they turn 65, but if you're not, you can apply for it independently.

- Citizenship or Legal Residency: To be eligible for Medicare Part B, you must be a U.S. citizen or a legal resident who has resided in the country continuously for a minimum of five years.

- Enrollment Period: The Initial Enrollment Period (IEP) is a seven-month window that includes the three months before your 65th birthday, the month of your birthday, and the three months following. It's generally advised to enroll during your IEP to evade potential penalties. If you're eligible due to disability, your IEP begins 21 months after you start receiving disability benefits.

- Premiums: Medicare Part B requires a monthly premium, usually deducted from your Social Security benefits. The premium amount may fluctuate each year and is income-dependent.

c. Medicare Part C: Medicare Advantage

Medicare Part C, also known as Medicare Advantage, is a healthcare plan provided by private insurers as an alternative method to obtain Medicare benefits. The eligibility and enrollment process for Medicare Part C involves several steps:

- Enrollment in Original Medicare: To be eligible for Medicare Part C, you must first enroll in Medicare Part A (hospital insurance) and Part B (medical insurance). Typically, individuals become eligible for Medicare at the age of 65. However, certain disabilities or medical conditions may qualify you for early eligibility.

• Residency in the Plan's Service Area: Medicare Advantage plans are only operational in specific service areas. Therefore, you must reside within the service area of a given Medicare Part C plan to qualify for it. It is important to verify the service area of the plan before enrollment.

• Enrollment during the Initial Enrollment Period (IEP): The IEP is a seven-month period that begins three months before and ends three months after the month you turn 65. This is generally the optimal time to enroll in Medicare Part C. If you miss your IEP, you may still enroll during the Annual Enrollment Period (AEP) or a Special Enrollment Period (SEP), provided you meet the eligibility criteria.

• Understanding Plan Options and Availability: The benefits, coverage, networks, and pricing of Medicare Advantage plans can vary. To find the plan that best suits your healthcare needs, it's essential to research and compare the options available in your area. Factors such as prices, deductibles, copayments, network providers, prescription drug coverage, and additional benefits (like dental or vision care) should all be considered.

• Direct Enrollment in a Medicare Advantage Plan: Unlike Original Medicare, which is administered by the federal government, Medicare Advantage plans are offered by private insurance companies. Once you've chosen a plan, you need to enroll directly with the insurance provider, who will guide you through the enrollment process and provide necessary paperwork and information.

• Adherence to Enrollment Deadlines: There are specific enrollment periods for Medicare Advantage plans, including the Annual Enrollment Period (AEP), which runs from October 15 to December 7 each year. It's crucial to enroll within these designated periods to avoid penalties or delays in coverage.

• Continuation of Part B Premium Payments: Even after enrolling in a Medicare Advantage plan, you're required to continue paying your Part B premium to the federal government. Medicare Advantage plans may also have their own additional premiums, so it's important to be aware of and fulfill any premium obligations.

d. Medicare Part D: Prescription Drug Coverage

To become eligible for Medicare Part D, the prescription drug coverage program provided by the U.S. government, you need to satisfy certain requirements. Here are the essential factors for eligibility:

• Enrollment in Original Medicare: Prior to qualifying for Medicare Part D, you need to be registered in either Part A or Part B of Original Medicare. Part B provides health insurance, while Part A offers hospital insurance. Together, they are commonly referred to as Original Medicare.

• Age and Health Status: Medicare Part D is primarily available to individuals who are 65 years or older. However, younger individuals with specific medical conditions or disabilities may also be eligible.

• U.S. Citizenship or Legal Residency: To be eligible for Medicare Part D, you must either be a U.S. citizen or a legal resident who has resided in the country for a minimum of five consecutive years.

• Enrollment Periods: Enrollment in Medicare Part D must occur during designated enrollment periods. The Initial Enrollment Period (IEP) is the first opportunity to register, typically starting three months before your 65th birthday and lasting for seven months. If you miss this period, you can enroll during the Annual Enrollment Period (AEP), which usually runs from October 15 to December 7 each year. Special Enrollment Periods (SEPs) are also available under certain circumstances, such as loss of employment coverage or relocation.

• Choosing a Prescription Drug Plan (PDP): Once you qualify for Medicare Part D, you need to select a PDP from the options available in your area. These plans are offered by private insurance providers that have been approved by Medicare. It's essential to thoroughly research and compare these plans, as each one has its own formulary (list of covered drugs) and premium rates, to find the one that best fits your needs.

CHAPTER 6: LIVING WITH MEDICARE

The phrase "Living with Medicare" pertains to the experience of being a participant in, and depending on, the Medicare program for healthcare coverage and services. We will delve into the experience of navigating through various facets of Medicare coverage.

1. Medicare Part A: Hospital Insurance

Being enrolled in Medicare Part A can offer individuals crucial health insurance coverage. Often referred to as "Hospital Insurance," Medicare Part A primarily encompasses inpatient hospital care, skilled nursing facility care, home healthcare, and hospice care. Let's delve into the advantages and expenses linked to Medicare Part A.

Advantages of Medicare Part A:

● Inpatient Hospital Care: Medicare Part A caters to the expenses related to hospitalization. This includes semi-private rooms, meals, nursing services, and essential hospital amenities such as surgeries, medications, and diagnostic evaluations.

• Skilled Nursing Facility (SNF) Care: If you need skilled nursing or rehabilitation services following a hospital stay, Medicare Part A covers the expenses of care in a skilled nursing facility. This includes skilled nursing services, physical therapy, speech-language pathology services, and occupational therapy.

• Home Healthcare: Medicare Part A offers coverage for eligible home healthcare services. This includes part-time skilled nursing care, therapy services, medical social services, and home health aide services. However, certain prerequisites must be fulfilled for coverage, such as being homebound and requiring skilled care.

• Hospice Care: Medicare Part A covers hospice care for individuals suffering from terminal illnesses. This includes medical, nursing, and support services to manage pain and symptoms, emotional and spiritual support, and respite care.

• Blood Transfusions: Medicare Part A caters to the expenses of blood transfusions received during a covered inpatient stay or as part of a Part B-covered outpatient service.

Expenses Associated with Medicare Part A:

1. Premiums:

Medicare Part A is often free of charge for those who have contributed to Medicare taxes during their employment years. This is commonly known as "premium-free Part A." However, if you don't meet the criteria for premium-free Part A, a monthly premium may be required. Here are some crucial points about Medicare Part A premiums:

● Premium-Free Part A: A large portion of Medicare recipients are eligible for premium-free Part A coverage. To qualify, one must have contributed to Medicare taxes for a minimum of 10 years (or 40 quarters) during their employment. This implies that their Medicare taxes during their working years cover the premium costs for Part A.

● Non-eligibility for Premium-Free Part A: Those who haven't worked the necessary 10 years might still qualify for Part A coverage, but they would need to pay a premium. If they have contributed to Medicare taxes for at least 7.5 years (or 30-39 quarters), they would pay a lower premium for Part A. For 2023, the reduced premium is $259 per month.

● Buy-In Premium: In certain situations, individuals who don't meet the criteria for premium-free or reduced premium Part A coverage may still be able to purchase Part A by paying a monthly premium. The buy-in premium amount varies depending on the individual's work history, residency, and other factors. The exact cost would need to be determined by contacting the Social Security Administration or the Centers for Medicare & Medicaid Services (CMS).

2. Deductibles:

Medicare Part A includes a deductible that must be paid before the coverage begins. The deductible amount can fluctuate each year. Once you've met the deductible, Medicare covers most of the costs of your inpatient hospital care for up to a certain number of days. Here are the specifics regarding the deductibles associated with Medicare Part A:

➢ Hospital Deductible (Inpatient Care):

● Each benefit period, which commences when you're admitted to a hospital or skilled nursing facility, has its own deductible.

● For 2023, the deductible for hospital stays is $1,548 per benefit period. This implies that if you're admitted to the hospital multiple times within the same benefit period, you only have to pay this deductible once.

➢ Skilled Nursing Facility (SNF) Deductible:

● The SNF deductible is also applicable per benefit period.

● In 2023, the deductible for a skilled nursing facility is $0. This means that you won't have to pay any deductible for the first 20 days of your stay in a Medicare-approved skilled nursing facility.

➢ Home Health Care Deductible:

● Medicare Part A covers some home healthcare services, including skilled nursing care, physical therapy, and speech-language pathology services, under certain conditions.

● However, there is no specific deductible for home health care services under Medicare Part A. The deductible applies primarily to inpatient hospital and skilled nursing facility care.

3. Coinsurance or Copayments:

After you've utilized your Medicare-covered hospital days, you may have to pay coinsurance or copayment amounts for each day beyond that limit. These costs can vary depending on the length of your stay and the specific services received. Coinsurance refers to the portion of the medical costs that you are responsible for paying after you have met your deductible. For Medicare Part A, the coinsurance is typically applied to inpatient hospital stays and skilled nursing facility care. Here's how it works:

➢ Inpatient Hospital Stays: For each benefit period, Medicare has a deductible that you must pay out-of-pocket before Medicare coverage begins. In 2023, the Part A deductible is $1,548 per benefit period. Once you have paid this deductible, Medicare covers the cost of your inpatient hospital stay for the first 60 days. However, starting from the 61st day up to the 90th day, you will be responsible for a daily coinsurance amount. In 2023, the daily coinsurance for days 61-90 is $387.

➢ Skilled Nursing Facility (SNF) Care: If you require skilled nursing care after a hospital stay, Medicare covers up to 100 days in a skilled nursing facility. Similar to inpatient hospital stays, for days 1-20, Medicare covers the full cost. However, for days 21-100, you are responsible for a daily coinsurance amount. In 2023, the daily coinsurance for days 21-100 is $193.50.

Copayments, also known as "copays," are fixed amounts you need to pay for specific services or supplies. Under Medicare Part A, copayments are typically associated with certain home health care services. If you receive home health care services approved by Medicare, you may be responsible for 20% of the Medicare-approved amount for durable medical equipment (DME) and supplies, such as wheelchairs or oxygen. The amount of the copayment varies depending on the specific item or service.

2. Medicare Part B: Medical Insurance

Being enrolled in Medicare Part B offers a plethora of advantages and comprehensive coverage for your healthcare requirements. Here's an in-depth examination of the benefits and expenses related to Medicare Part B.

Advantages of Medicare Part B:

• Medical Consultations: Medicare Part B encompasses a broad spectrum of medical services offered by physicians, encompassing routine visits, expert advice, and preventive healthcare services such as health screenings and immunizations.

• Specialist Medical Care: Part B also includes services rendered by specialist doctors, like cardiologists, dermatologists, and oncologists. This guarantees that you have access to the specialized medical attention you may require for specific health issues.

• Outpatient Medical Services: Medicare Part B provides coverage for essential outpatient services, such as diagnostic examinations, laboratory procedures, X-rays, MRIs, and CT scans. It also covers treatments like chemotherapy, radiation therapy, and dialysis.

• Preventive Healthcare Services: Part B offers coverage for a variety of preventive healthcare services aimed at early detection and prevention of diseases. This includes screenings for conditions like cancer, diabetes, and cardiovascular diseases.

● Ambulance Services: Medicare Part B provides coverage for emergency ambulance transport when it is deemed medically necessary, such as in instances of accidents or sudden severe illness.

● Durable Medical Equipment (DME): Part B contributes towards the cost of durable medical equipment, such as wheelchairs, walkers, oxygen equipment, and certain types of prosthetic devices.

● Mental Health Services: Medicare Part B offers coverage for mental health services, including outpatient therapy and counseling sessions.

● Home Healthcare: Part B provides coverage for certain essential home healthcare services, such as intermittent skilled nursing care, physical therapy, and occupational therapy.

Expenses Associated with Medicare Part B:

1. Monthly Premiums:

Recipients of Medicare Part B are required to pay a monthly premium. The premium amount, which may change annually, is typically subtracted from your Social Security benefits. Your exact premium is calculated based on your income and may be subject to income-related monthly adjustment amounts (IRMAA) if your income surpasses certain limits. Premiums for Medicare Part B can fluctuate based on various factors, including income, marital status, and the year of enrollment. These premiums are usually adjusted on a yearly basis. For the majority of beneficiaries, the standard premium amount for Medicare Part B is established each year by the Centers for Medicare & Medicaid Services (CMS). The standard premium for Medicare Part B is currently $148.50 per month, though it's essential to confirm the most recent premium amounts as they may have changed.

It should be noted that some beneficiaries might pay more than the standard premium amount based on their income, referred to as the income-related monthly adjustment amount (IRMAA). The IRMAA is an extra amount that higher-income individuals and couples pay in addition to the standard premium. The income thresholds for determining the IRMAA are adjusted annually. Beneficiaries with higher incomes are required to pay a larger portion of the total cost of Medicare Part B.

2. Annual Deductible:

Medicare Part B includes an annual deductible that must be fulfilled before Medicare begins covering its share. The deductible amount may change each year and is generally reasonable.

Deductibles are the sum of money you must pay out-of-pocket before Medicare Part B begins covering services. They serve as a form of cost-sharing between the beneficiary and the government. Here are some details about deductibles for Medicare Part B:

➢ Annual Deductible: Medicare Part B has an annual deductible, implying you are responsible for paying a certain amount each year before your coverage kicks in. The deductible is adjusted annually and is subject to change. The standard Part B deductible is $203 per year. However, it's crucial to note that deductible amounts may change in the future, so it's always best to consult official sources or contact Medicare for the most current information.

➢ What Counts Towards the Deductible: The Part B deductible applies to most services and supplies covered under Medicare Part B. This includes doctor visits, outpatient therapy, laboratory tests, diagnostic screenings, ambulance services, medical equipment, and certain preventive services. It's crucial to review the specific coverage guidelines and consult with healthcare providers to ensure that the services you receive are eligible for deductible consideration.

➢ What Does Not Count Towards the Deductible: Certain services are not subject to the Part B deductible. For instance, preventive services like flu shots, cancer screenings, and certain vaccinations are generally exempt from the deductible. Additionally, services provided by healthcare professionals who don't accept Medicare assignment may have different billing arrangements, and the deductible may not apply in those cases.

➢ Timing and Reset: The annual deductible for Medicare Part B is generally reset at the beginning of each calendar year, on January 1st. This means that once you have paid the full deductible amount, you won't have to pay it again until the next year. However, it's crucial to note that deductibles may change annually, so it's wise to verify the amount each year.

It's worth noting that some individuals may have their Medicare Part B premiums and/or deductibles covered or reduced through programs like Medicaid, Medicare Savings Programs, or employer-sponsored retiree health plans. Additionally, Medigap (Medicare Supplement) plans can help cover Part B deductibles and coinsurance for those who choose to enroll in them.

3. Coinsurance or Copayments:

After fulfilling the deductible, you are responsible for paying a coinsurance or copayment for most Medicare Part B services. Typically, Medicare covers 80% of the approved amount for services, and you are responsible for the remaining 20%.

For instance, if the Medicare-approved amount for a doctor's visit is $100, Medicare will cover $80 (80% of $100), and you'll be responsible for the remaining $20 as coinsurance.

4. Excess Charges:

In some instances, healthcare providers who accept Medicare may charge more than the Medicare-approved amount for a service. If this occurs, you may be responsible for paying the excess charges out of pocket.

It's crucial to remember that there are numerous income-based assistance options and programs available to help individuals with low incomes cover their Medicare Part B premiums and other related expenses.

3. Medicare Part C: Medicare Advantage

Medicare Type C amalgamates the benefits of Medicare Part A (hospital insurance) and Part B (medical insurance), supplemented with additional perks offered by private insurance firms approved by Medicare. This discourse will outline the advantages and expenses linked with Medicare Type C.

Advantages of Medicare Type C:

➢ Extensive Coverage: Medicare Type C plans generally provide the same coverage as Original Medicare (Part A and Part B), encompassing hospital admissions, doctor consultations, preventive healthcare, and essential medical services.

➢ Supplementary Benefits: Medicare Type C plans frequently offer extra benefits not covered by Original Medicare. These added perks may encompass prescription drug coverage (Medicare Part D), vision care, dental care, hearing aids, fitness programs, and other wellness services.

➢ Coordinated Healthcare: Medicare Type C plans are managed care plans that typically incorporate a network of healthcare providers. They may have preferred networks or necessitate referrals for specialist care. The benefit is that these plans coordinate care among providers, ensuring consistency and potentially minimizing paperwork for beneficiaries.

➤ Maximum Out-of-Pocket Limit: Medicare Type C plans establish a yearly limit on out-of-pocket expenses, which is the highest amount you'll have to pay for covered services in a calendar year. Once you reach this limit, the plan covers 100% of covered services for the rest of the year.

➤ Cost Efficiency: Medicare Type C plans can sometimes offer cost savings compared to Original Medicare. They may have lower monthly premiums, although some plans have additional premiums on top of the Part B premium. Copayments and coinsurance for services can also be lower in Medicare Advantage plans, making healthcare more economical for beneficiaries.

Expenses Associated with Medicare Type C:

1.   **Monthly Premiums:**

The monthly premiums for Medicare Type C plans can vary significantly. Some plans may not require any additional premium beyond the standard Medicare Part B premium, while others may necessitate an extra premium. The cost of this premium is contingent on numerous factors, including the specific plan, coverage options, geographical location, and the insurance company providing the plan. Certain Medicare Advantage plans do not require any additional premium beyond the Part B premium. However, other plans may require premiums that range from a nominal amount to several hundred dollars per month.

2.   Deductibles and Copayments:

Similar to Original Medicare, Medicare Type C plans often include deductibles and copayments for certain services. The specific amounts vary between plans, making it crucial to review the plan details to understand the costs associated with specific services.

Here are some key details about deductibles in Medicare Type C:

➤ Plan Variations: Deductibles can fluctuate based on the specific Medicare Type C plan you opt for. Each insurance company offering Medicare Type C plans sets its own deductible amounts within the guidelines established by the Centers for Medicare & Medicaid Services (CMS). Therefore, it's crucial to meticulously review the details of each plan to understand the deductible amounts and how they apply.

➤ Different Deductibles: Medicare Type C plans can have different types of deductibles. The two common types are medical deductibles and drug deductibles. Medical deductibles apply to services covered under Part A and Part B, such as hospital stays, doctor visits, and medical procedures. Drug deductibles, on the other hand, apply to prescription drug coverage under Medicare Type C plans that include it.

➤ Annual Limits: Medicare Type C plans that include deductibles typically have an annual limit on the total amount you'll need to pay out of pocket for deductibles and other cost-sharing expenses. Once you reach this limit, the plan will cover the remaining costs for covered services for the rest of the year. It's important to note that the annual limit may vary between plans, so it's essential to check the details of each plan.

➤ Cost-Sharing Structure: Deductibles are part of the overall cost-sharing structure in Medicare Type C plans. In addition to deductibles, you may also have other cost-sharing responsibilities such as copayments (fixed amounts you pay for each service or prescription) and coinsurance (a percentage of the cost you're responsible for).

➤ Plan Specifics: The deductible amounts and how they are applied can vary from plan to plan. Some plans may have separate deductibles for medical services and prescription drugs, while others may have a combined deductible. The deductible may apply to all covered services or only specific services, depending on the plan.

➤ Network Considerations: Medicare Type C plans often have provider networks, which means you may need to use doctors, hospitals, and other healthcare providers within the plan's network to receive full coverage. Some plans may have separate deductibles for in-network and out-of-network services, so it's important to understand how the deductible applies based on the providers you choose.

3.   **Network Restrictions:**

Medicare Type C plans usually have a network of healthcare providers, and using out-of-network providers may result in higher costs or limited coverage. It's crucial to check the plan's network and ensure that preferred providers are accessible in your area.

Network restrictions in Medicare Advantage plans refer to the limitations on accessing healthcare providers and facilities outside of the plan's network. These restrictions can vary depending on the specific Medicare Advantage plan and the insurance company offering it. Here are some common types of network restrictions that may be associated with Medicare Advantage plans:

➤ Health Maintenance Organization (HMO) Plans: HMO plans typically have a network of healthcare providers, including doctors, hospitals, and specialists, with whom the plan has contracted. In most cases, you are required to receive care from providers within the plan's network, except in emergencies or urgent situations. You may also need to select a primary care physician (PCP) who coordinates your care and provides referrals to specialists within the network.

➢ Preferred Provider Organization (PPO) Plans: PPO plans offer more flexibility compared to HMO plans. They have a network of preferred providers, but you have the option to seek care from out-of-network providers as well, although it may come at a higher cost. If you choose to see an out-of-network provider, you will typically pay higher coinsurance or copayments.

➢ Exclusive Provider Organization (EPO) Plans: EPO plans are similar to HMO plans in that they usually require you to receive care within the plan's network. However, EPO plans do not require a PCP or referrals for specialist care. If you receive care outside the network in non-emergency situations, you may be responsible for the full cost.

➢ Point of Service (POS) Plans: HMO and PPO policies are combined in POS plans. You are often required to select a primary care physician from within the network, but you do have the option to see a provider outside the network, however this usually entails paying more out-of-pocket.

It's recommended to carefully review the network restrictions, provider directories, and coverage details of any Medicare Advantage plan you are considering to understand how it may affect your access to healthcare providers and facilities.

4.   Prior Authorization:

Prior authorization may be necessary under some Medicare Type C plans for specific services or treatments. Prior authorization, often called pre-authorization or pre-certification, is a technique used by Medicare and other health insurance plans to ascertain whether a certain service, medicine, or medical procedure satisfies the requirements for coverage. It is a technique for the insurance company to confirm that the requested service is reasonable and medically essential before agreeing to pay for it.

The following steps are often included in the prior authorization process:

• Prescribing or recommending the service: A healthcare provider, such as a doctor or specialist, determines that a particular service, medication, or procedure is necessary for the patient's medical condition or treatment.

• Checking coverage and requirements: The healthcare provider or their staff contacts the patient's insurance plan to determine if prior authorization is required for the requested service. They also review the specific requirements and criteria set by Medicare or the Medicare Advantage plan.

• Submitting the prior authorization request: If prior authorization is required, the healthcare provider or their staff completes a prior authorization request form, which includes relevant clinical information about the patient's condition, medical history, and the proposed treatment. This information helps the insurance provider evaluate the medical necessity of the requested service.

• Review and decision: The insurance provider's utilization review department or a designated third-party organization reviews the prior authorization request. They assess whether the requested service meets the coverage criteria outlined by Medicare or the Medicare Advantage plan. This review may involve medical professionals who specialize in the relevant field.

• Approval or denial: Based on the review, the insurance provider communicates the decision to the healthcare provider and the patient. If the prior authorization request is approved, the service is deemed medically necessary, and the insurance provider agrees to cover the cost as specified in the patient's plan. If the request is denied, the healthcare provider and the patient are notified, and alternative options may be explored.

It's important to note that the specific prior authorization requirements can vary depending on the type of service or medication being requested, the patient's Medicare plan, and other factors.

5.   Service Limitations:

Although Medicare Type C plans often offer additional benefits, these benefits may have limitations or restrictions. For example, vision or dental coverage may only cover specific services or have annual maximums on benefits. It's essential to understand the details of the plan to ensure the coverage meets your specific healthcare needs.

4. Medicare Part D: Prescription Drug Coverage

Medicare Part D aids in offsetting the expenses of prescription drugs, ensuring beneficiaries can access necessary medications.

Advantages of Medicare Part D:

• Comprehensive Prescription Drug Coverage: Medicare Part D provides extensive coverage for a diverse array of prescription drugs, encompassing both brand-name and generic medications. This coverage significantly reduces the out-of-pocket expenses related to the procurement of prescription drugs.

• Access to a Comprehensive Drug List: Each Medicare Part D plan includes a formulary, a comprehensive list of covered drugs. While the formulary varies from plan to plan, it typically encompasses a wide range of medications for various health conditions. Access to a formulary ensures that beneficiaries can secure the drugs they require.

• Flexibility in Plan Selection: Medicare Part D offers beneficiaries the flexibility to choose from a variety of Prescription Drug Plans (PDPs) provided by private insurance companies. This flexibility allows individuals to select a plan that best aligns with their specific medication requirements and budget constraints.

• Coverage during the Coverage Gap ("Donut Hole"): Medicare Part D includes a coverage gap, colloquially known as the "donut hole." During this gap, beneficiaries receive discounts on both brand-name and generic drugs. The coverage gap is gradually closing, with beneficiaries receiving increasing discounts until they reach the catastrophic coverage threshold.

• Catastrophic Coverage: Upon reaching the catastrophic coverage threshold, Medicare Part D provides additional cost assistance. In this phase, beneficiaries are required to pay only a minimal copayment or coinsurance amount for their covered medications.

Expenses Associated with Medicare Part D:

1. Monthly Premium:

Medicare Part D plans necessitate a monthly premium, the amount of which may fluctuate based on the chosen plan. This premium is an extra expense that beneficiaries must bear to retain their prescription drug coverage. Factors such as the degree of coverage, the drugs included, and the insurance provider offering the plan can influence the premium amount. Premiums can range from approximately $10 to over $100 monthly. For those with higher incomes, there may be an additional charge known as the Income-Related Monthly Adjustment Amount (IRMAA). IRMAA is an extra sum added to the monthly premium, determined by the beneficiary's modified adjusted gross income (MAGI) from two years prior. The income thresholds for IRMAA can change annually, making it crucial to check the current guidelines. A late enrollment penalty may apply if you don't enroll in a Medicare Part D plan when first eligible. This penalty is added to your monthly premium and could permanently increase the cost.

2. Deductible:

Some Medicare Part D plans include an annual deductible, which is the amount beneficiaries must pay for prescription medications before the plan's coverage commences. Not all Part D plans have a deductible, and some may offer a $0 deductible. Each year, Medicare sets a maximum deductible limit for Part D plans, and no plan can have a deductible higher than this limit. Once you have paid your deductible amount, you enter the deductible phase, during which you are responsible for paying the initial costs of your prescription drugs until you reach the initial coverage limit set by your plan. Once your out-of-pocket spending reaches a certain threshold, you enter the catastrophic coverage stage, where you pay significantly less for your prescription drugs.

3. Copayments/Coinsurance:

In addition to the monthly premium, beneficiaries must pay copayments or coinsurance when purchasing prescription medications. Coinsurance is a portion of the cost of the prescription, whereas copayments are fixed amounts determined by the plan. Prescription drug coverage is often divided into multiple Medicare Part D plan tiers, each with a different copayment or coinsurance rate. These tiers classify medications according to their price and therapeutic value. The coinsurance or copayment levels for each tier may vary across different Part D plans. Beneficiaries must carefully read each plan's fine print to understand the exact copayment or coinsurance amounts related to the prescription medications they require.

4. Coverage Gap (Donut Hole):

The coverage gap refers to a temporary limit on prescription drug coverage that may affect some Medicare beneficiaries. While the coverage gap has been closing, beneficiaries may still have to pay a higher percentage of their prescription drug costs during this phase. However, the discounts received during this period help reduce the financial burden. The coverage gap begins after a beneficiary and their drug plan have spent a certain amount of money on covered prescription drugs in a calendar year. Once the total drug costs reach a pre-determined threshold, the beneficiary enters the coverage gap. In this gap, the beneficiary is responsible for a higher portion of their prescription drug costs. Not all prescription drugs are affected by the coverage gap, and Medicare requires drug plans to offer some coverage during the gap period. The coverage gap ends when the beneficiary's out-of-pocket spending on prescription drugs reaches a certain limit. At this point, they enter the catastrophic coverage phase, where Medicare provides additional coverage, and the beneficiary pays a smaller coinsurance or copayment for their medications for the rest of the year. The coverage gap has been gradually closing due to changes introduced by the Affordable Care Act (ACA), which aims to eliminate the coverage gap entirely.

5.   Exclusions in Medication Coverage:

Medicare Part D does not encompass all prescription drugs. Some medications may be omitted from the formulary, necessitating beneficiaries to bear the entire cost themselves or seek alternative coverage solutions.

Although Medicare Part D covers a broad spectrum of medications, there are certain drug categories that are typically not included. These medications are classified into several categories:

● Over-the-Counter (OTC) Drugs: Medicare Part D generally does not cover most OTC drugs, which are medications that can be acquired without a prescription. OTC drugs include pain relievers such as aspirin or ibuprofen, cough and cold remedies, and allergy medications. However, there are exceptions, such as certain OTC drugs prescribed by a doctor.

● Prescription Vitamins and Minerals: Medicare Part D usually does not cover prescription-grade vitamins and minerals, except in specific circumstances. These may include instances where a vitamin or mineral is prescribed to treat a specific medical condition or if it is deemed a necessary component of a covered medication.

● Cosmetic Purpose Drugs: Medicare Part D does not cover medications primarily used for cosmetic purposes. This includes treatments for hair growth, wrinkle creams, and other similar products that are not deemed medically necessary.

● Weight Loss or Gain Medications: Medicare Part D typically does not cover prescription drugs used for weight loss or weight gain. This includes medications like appetite suppressants or drugs used to induce weight gain in certain medical conditions.

● Erectile Dysfunction Drugs: Medicare Part D generally does not cover prescription drugs used to treat erectile dysfunction. These medications include Viagra, Cialis, and Levitra.

• Fertility Drugs: Medicare Part D does not cover medications used for fertility treatments, such as drugs used in assisted reproductive technologies or hormone therapies for infertility.

• Experimental or Investigational Drugs: Medicare Part D does not cover medications considered experimental or investigational. These are drugs still undergoing clinical trials or not yet approved by the U.S. Food and Drug Administration (FDA).

While these categories typically represent drugs not covered by Medicare Part D, exceptions may apply in certain circumstances. Furthermore, coverage may vary based on the specific Medicare Part D plan chosen, as some plans may offer additional coverage beyond the minimum criteria. Therefore, beneficiaries are advised to thoroughly review the terms of their Medicare Part D plan to understand the coverage and any potential limitations or exclusions.

With Medicare, you gain access to a comprehensive network of doctors, specialists, hospitals, and healthcare providers, ensuring you receive necessary medical care when needed. Medicare also covers preventive services like screenings and vaccinations to help maintain your health and identify potential issues early.

In conclusion, while Medicare covers a significant portion of your medical costs, it doesn't cover everything. Out-of-pocket expenses such as deductibles, coinsurance, and copayments may still be your responsibility. Consider Medigap policies, which can provide additional coverage for services not fully covered by Medicare, to help offset these costs.

Medicare Advantage (Part C) plans, offered by private insurance providers approved by Medicare, should also be considered. These plans often provide additional benefits such as vision, dental, and hearing coverage, and may also include prescription drug coverage. While Original Medicare is an option, Medicare Advantage plans offer an alternative. Thoroughly research and compare different plans to ensure they align with your unique healthcare needs.

Stay updated with any changes or modifications to the program to maximize your Medicare benefits. Regularly reviewing your plan and being aware of available options allows you to make informed decisions about your healthcare. Medicare policies and coverage can change over time.

Lastly, proactive preventative care and maintaining a healthy lifestyle can help optimize your overall health while managing your healthcare costs. By staying active, eating healthily, and having regular checkups, you can prioritize your health and potentially prevent or manage chronic diseases.

In summary, having Medicare during retirement can provide crucial healthcare coverage. By understanding the various aspects of Medicare, exploring other options, and focusing on preventive care, you can maximize its benefits and secure a healthier future.

CHAPTER 7: TEN MEDICARE MISTAKES TO AVOID

Medicare is a vital health insurance program in the United States for individuals aged 65 and above. While Medicare provides essential coverage, people often make common mistakes when navigating its complexities. Maximizing your Medicare benefits can be achieved by avoiding these pitfalls. Here are ten common Medicare mistakes to steer clear of:

1. Delaying Medicare enrollment: If you're eligible for Medicare, failing to enroll during your Initial Enrollment Period (IEP) can lead to late enrollment penalties and coverage gaps. Stay informed about enrollment deadlines to avoid these issues.

2. Choosing the wrong Medicare plan: Medicare offers various coverage options, including Original Medicare (Parts A and B), Medicare Advantage (Part C), and prescription drug coverage (Part D). It's vital to evaluate your healthcare needs and select the plan that best suits them.

3. Neglecting annual coverage reassessment: Medicare plans can change their benefits, costs, and provider networks each year. Failing to review your plan annually could lead to unexpected expenses or inadequate coverage. Use the Annual Enrollment Period (AEP) to assess your options and make necessary changes.

4. Overlooking the "Medicare Advantage Disenrollment Period": If you're enrolled in a Medicare Advantage plan and find it unsuitable, you can switch to Original Medicare during the Medicare Advantage Disenrollment Period (January 1 to February 14). Missing this period could limit your options.

5. Failing to research prescription drug plans: If you require prescription medications, choosing the right Part D plan is essential. Each plan has a formulary detailing the covered drugs and their costs. To find the most cost-effective option, compare plans based on your medication needs.

6. Skipping "Welcome to Medicare" preventive services: Upon enrolling in Medicare, you're entitled to several free preventive services, including screenings and vaccines. Utilize these services to detect potential health issues early and take appropriate action.

7. Ignoring coverage gaps: Medicare's cost-sharing obligations include deductibles, copayments, and coinsurance. Failing to budget for these out-of-pocket costs could lead to unexpected financial strain. Consider additional insurance, like Medigap plans, to bridge these coverage gaps.

8. Not updating income details: Medicare premiums for higher-income earners are subject to an Income-Related Monthly Adjustment Amount (IRMAA). To ensure accurate premium calculations, promptly inform the Social Security Administration of any income changes.

9. Neglecting "Extra Help" for prescription drugs: The Low-Income Subsidy (LIS) program, also known as Extra Help, assists low-income individuals with prescription drug costs. Many eligible individuals fail to apply for this program, which can increase their medication expenses.

10. Hesitating to seek help: Medicare can be complex, making it easy to make mistakes or overlook crucial details. Don't hesitate to seek assistance from reliable sources like Medicare.gov, SHIP, or registered insurance agents specializing in Medicare.

By avoiding these common Medicare mistakes and staying informed, you can leverage the benefits offered by Medicare and make knowledgeable decisions about your healthcare coverage.

CHAPTER 8: Knowing Your Rights

As a member of Medicare, it is crucial to understand your rights and entitlements under this program to ensure you receive the necessary healthcare services and benefits. This chapter aims to discuss the various rights that Medicare beneficiaries possess, empowering them to make informed decisions about their healthcare.

While Medicare clients have various rights and protections, here are ten important rights for Medicare clients:

1. Right to Information

The Right to Information (RTI) is a fundamental privilege that empowers individuals to access data maintained by public authorities. In the realm of Medicare recipients, the RTI is instrumental in promoting transparency, accountability, and empowerment for patients and healthcare consumers. Here is an exploration of the Right to Information for Medicare recipients:

• Access to Medical Records: Medicare recipients are entitled to request and access their medical records, encompassing information about their diagnoses, treatments, medications, test results, and other pertinent medical data. This access enables patients to be thoroughly informed about their healthcare decisions, seek alternative opinions, and actively engage in their treatment plans.

• Transparency in Healthcare Processes: The RTI empowers Medicare recipients to request information about various healthcare processes and policies. They can inquire about the protocols for accessing specific treatments, eligibility criteria for certain services, and any other relevant data that can influence their healthcare choices. Transparency in these areas assists patients in making informed decisions and holding healthcare providers accountable.

• Billing and Financial Information: Medicare recipients are entitled to acquire details about billing, costs, and financial aspects of their healthcare. They can request information about the charges for specific procedures, medications, or hospital stays. Access to billing and financial data ensures that patients comprehend the costs associated with their care and can address any discrepancies or concerns.

• Complaints and Grievance Procedures: The RTI empowers Medicare recipients to access information about the complaints and grievance procedures within the healthcare system. This includes details on how to lodge a complaint, the investigation process, and the steps taken to address grievances. Access to this information enables clients to express their concerns and seek suitable resolutions.

• Quality of Care and Performance Data: Medicare recipients are entitled to access information related to the quality of care provided by healthcare facilities and providers. This includes data on patient outcomes, infection rates, accreditation status, and performance indicators. Such data empowers patients to make informed choices about their healthcare providers and facilities, fostering a culture of accountability and improvement within the healthcare system.

• Privacy and Data Protection: The RTI also includes the right to privacy and data protection. Medicare recipients are entitled to know how their personal and medical data is collected, stored, used, and shared. They can request information about data security measures, consent requirements, and policies related to the handling of their sensitive data.

2. Right to Choose Providers

The ability of Medicare beneficiaries to select their preferred healthcare providers within the Medicare program is known as the right to choose providers for Medicare users. Medicare beneficiaries have the freedom to choose any healthcare provider they want, including general practitioners, specialists, hospitals, and other healthcare institutions. Beneficiaries are empowered to select the healthcare professionals they believe will best meet their needs and preferences. If a Medicare beneficiary is dissatisfied with their current care or simply prefers a different provider, they have the flexibility to change at any point.

The privilege to choose a healthcare provider is essential as it enables Medicare beneficiaries to actively engage in their healthcare decisions. It recognizes that each individual has unique healthcare needs and preferences, and provides them with the opportunity to seek providers that align with their needs.

When choosing providers, Medicare recipients may consider a variety of factors. These include the provider's qualifications and experience, the facility's accessibility and location, the quality of care provided, the clinician's communication style, and any personal recommendations or referrals from trusted sources.

While Medicare grants recipients the liberty to choose their healthcare providers, it's important to note that there are certain limitations and considerations to bear in mind. For instance, not all providers accept Medicare patients, and Medicare has specific payment policies. Additionally, some services may require prior authorization or referrals from a primary care physician.

In conclusion, the ability to choose providers is a fundamental aspect of the Medicare program. It empowers beneficiaries to make healthcare decisions and ensures that they can access healthcare professionals that best meet their needs. By allowing individuals to choose their healthcare providers, Medicare promotes personalized care and patient-centered healthcare delivery.

3. Right to Access Medically Necessary Services

Ensuring access to vital medical services for elderly and disabled citizens is a fundamental aspect of healthcare provision in many countries, including the United States. Medicare beneficiaries are entitled to avail themselves of services considered "medically necessary," defined as any healthcare services or supplies needed to prevent, diagnose, or treat a health condition. The program covers a wide range of services, including hospital care, doctor consultations, preventative health screenings, prescription medications, and more.

However, it's important to note that not all services or treatments are deemed medically necessary under Medicare. For example, the program does not cover elective or experimental procedures. Additionally, there can be variations in the interpretation of medical necessity, and coverage decisions can sometimes appear arbitrary. Nevertheless, the appeals process provides beneficiaries with an avenue to challenge such decisions and seek a review from an alternative authority.

Overall, Medicare's primary objective is to ensure that beneficiaries receive the necessary medical care to maintain their health and well-being, including access to medically necessary treatments. Policymakers and regulators continuously strive to strike a balance between ensuring access to vital services, managing costs, and maintaining the sustainability of the Medicare program.

4. The right to quality care

The entitlement to superior healthcare is a vital element of the healthcare system, especially for Medicare beneficiaries.

Accessibility, effectiveness, safety, and patient-centricity are integral to providing top-tier medical treatment for Medicare patients.

• Accessibility is paramount in ensuring quality care for Medicare beneficiaries. This implies that healthcare services and providers should be readily available and accessible to all qualifying individuals. Medicare beneficiaries should have a broad spectrum of healthcare services at their disposal, including primary care, specialists, hospitals, preventive care, and prescription medications. Moreover, proactive measures should be taken to overcome any obstacles to access, such as geographical or financial constraints.

• The effectiveness of care is another crucial element. Medicare beneficiaries are entitled to receive medically necessary treatments and interventions based on evidence. This necessitates healthcare providers to stay abreast of the latest research and guidelines to deliver the most effective care. The utilization of clinical decision support tools, electronic health records, and care coordination can enhance the effectiveness of care provided to Medicare beneficiaries.

• Safety is a fundamental cornerstone of quality care. Medicare beneficiaries have the right to be safeguarded from harm while availing healthcare services. This encompasses measures to prevent medical errors, infections, falls, and other adverse events. Healthcare facilities and providers should comply with stringent safety standards and constantly monitor and enhance patient safety practices.

• Patient-centricity is a key tenet in providing quality care for Medicare beneficiaries. This signifies that the care provided should be customized to the individual's needs, preferences, and values. Medicare beneficiaries should be actively involved in decision-making processes, have access to information about their care, and receive support for self-management of their health conditions. Respect for patient autonomy and dignity should be at the heart of the care provided to Medicare beneficiaries.

To uphold the right to quality care for Medicare beneficiaries, continuous monitoring, evaluation, and quality improvement initiatives are essential. Medicare employs various mechanisms, such as quality reporting programs, pay-for-performance models, and public reporting of quality measures, to evaluate and enhance the quality of care provided to its beneficiaries. These efforts are designed to motivate healthcare providers to deliver superior care and improve health outcomes for Medicare beneficiaries.

5. Right to Appeal Decisions

The opportunity to contest decisions is a vital aspect of the Medicare program, ensuring beneficiaries can challenge the determinations made about their healthcare coverage and services. Beneficiaries can leverage the appeals process to seek a review of unfavorable decisions, potentially leading to these decisions being reversed.

Beneficiaries have the following entitlements to challenge Medicare's decisions:

• Refusal of coverage: If Medicare refuses to cover a specific service, treatment, or medication, beneficiaries have the entitlement to contest the decision. This may include situations where Medicare deems a particular treatment medically unnecessary or a specific medication not covered under the beneficiary's plan.

• Cessation of services: If Medicare decides to cease or reduce services currently provided to a beneficiary, they have the entitlement to contest the decision. This could relate to situations where Medicare determines that ongoing services are no longer medically necessary, or there is a change in the beneficiary's health status affecting the required level of care.

• Payment disputes: If Medicare declines to pay for a service or rejects a reimbursement claim, beneficiaries have the entitlement to contest the decision. This could happen if Medicare determines a service is not covered, or there are billing or coding discrepancies that need resolution.

Typically, Medicare beneficiaries follow a multi-step appeals process, providing several opportunities to present their case:

1.   Redetermination: The initial step involves requesting a redetermination, asking the Medicare contractor to reassess the decision within a specified timeframe after the initial determination.

2.   Reconsideration: If the redetermination is unfavorable, beneficiaries can request a reconsideration by a Qualified Independent Contractor (QIC) uninvolved in the initial decision. The QIC will carry out an independent review of the case.

3.   Administrative Law Judge (ALJ) Hearing: If the reconsideration decision is unfavorable, beneficiaries can request a hearing before an ALJ. This step involves presenting the case to an independent judge who will assess the evidence and render a decision.

4.   Medicare Appeals Council Review: If the ALJ decision is unfavorable, beneficiaries can request a review by the Medicare Appeals Council. The Council will scrutinize the case and decide whether to affirm, amend, or overturn the ALJ's decision.

5.   Judicial Review: If the Medicare Appeals Council's decision is unsatisfactory, beneficiaries have the entitlement to file a lawsuit in federal district court for further review of their case.

It's important to note that the appeals process can be complex and lengthy. Beneficiaries have the right to representation at all stages of the appeals process, and Medicare is obligated to carry out prompt and impartial reviews of appeals.

If a beneficiary disagrees with a Medicare decision, it is advisable to seek guidance on navigating the appeals process from the Medicare helpline or a certified healthcare advocate.

6. Right to Privacy

Privacy is a vital aspect of healthcare, particularly for Medicare beneficiaries. It is essential to maintain the confidentiality of individual health data, ensuring patients feel comfortable seeking and receiving medical treatment.

The Health Insurance Portability and Accountability Act (HIPAA) in the United States sets federal standards to protect the privacy and security of personal health information. Entities such as healthcare providers, health plans, and other organizations dealing with protected health information must adhere to these standards.

HIPAA, along with other relevant laws and regulations, upholds the privacy rights of Medicare patients. Here are some key aspects of these privacy rights for Medicare beneficiaries:

● Confidentiality of Health Information: Medicare beneficiaries can expect their personal health information, including details about their medical conditions, treatments, prescriptions, and other sensitive data, to remain confidential.

● Consent and Authorization: Before disclosing health information to others, Medicare beneficiaries must give their informed consent. There are certain exceptions for treatment, payment, and healthcare operations. Generally, written authorization is needed for disclosures beyond these purposes.

● Access to Personal Health Information: Medicare beneficiaries have the right to access and obtain a copy of their personal health information held by healthcare providers or health plans. They can also request amendments to their records if they find errors or omissions.

● Security Safeguards: Healthcare providers and health plans must implement security measures to protect the health information of Medicare beneficiaries from unauthorized access, use, or disclosure. This includes physical, administrative, and technical safeguards such as secure electronic systems and restricted access to medical records.

● Notice of Privacy Practices: Medicare beneficiaries should receive a notice of privacy practices from their healthcare providers or health plans. This notice outlines how their health information will be used and disclosed, as well as their rights concerning their information.

While privacy rights are protected, it's important to note that there are certain circumstances where healthcare providers may be legally obligated to disclose specific information, such as complying with court orders or notifying public health authorities about certain infectious diseases.

7. Right to Non-Discrimination

The principle of non-discrimination is a cornerstone in healthcare, ensuring that every individual, irrespective of their distinct characteristics or circumstances, receives equitable treatment and equal access to services. This principle is particularly pertinent for Medicare beneficiaries, often comprising elderly individuals or those with disabilities who rely on the Medicare program for their healthcare needs.

It's worth noting that legislation such as the Civil Rights Act of 1964, the Age Discrimination Act of 1975, and the Americans with Disabilities Act (ADA) of 1990, among others, prohibit discrimination and apply to Medicare. These laws play a pivotal role in safeguarding Medicare beneficiaries from bias, thereby facilitating their access to equitable healthcare.

Medicare beneficiaries who believe they have been subjected to discrimination can seek assistance from their State Health Insurance Assistance Program (SHIP) or lodge a complaint with the Office for Civil Rights (OCR) within the Department of Health and Human Services (HHS).

Regardless of their age, disability, race, ethnicity, gender, or any other protected status, it is imperative that Medicare beneficiaries are assured their right to non-discrimination, thereby ensuring their fair and equal access to healthcare services.

8. Right to participate in care decisions

Numerous statutes and guidelines uphold the entitlement of Medicare recipients to engage in their healthcare decisions, a vital aspect of patient-focused care. Here are some pivotal points concerning the right of Medicare recipients to be involved in their healthcare decisions:

● Informed Consent: Medicare recipients are entitled to comprehensive information about their health condition, potential treatments, associated risks and benefits, and alternative therapies. This empowers individuals to make educated decisions about their healthcare. It is the responsibility of healthcare practitioners to convey this information in a way that the patient can understand.

● Collaborative Decision-Making: Medicare recipients are entitled to actively participate in choosing their healthcare options. To achieve this, the patient and their healthcare provider must collaborate. The patient's values, preferences, and goals should be considered when deciding on their care plan.

● Advance Directives: Medicare recipients can prepare advance directives, like living wills or durable powers of attorney for healthcare, specifying their healthcare preferences in case they are unable to express them personally. Healthcare providers must respect and adhere to these directives.

● Medicare recipients who are incapable of making their own healthcare decisions can appoint a representative, such as a relative or a close friend, to act on their behalf. To act in the patient's best interest, the representative should be involved in the decision-making process for their care.

● Appeals and Complaints: Medicare recipients have the right to challenge decisions related to their treatment. They can lodge an appeal or complaint to request a review and potential reversal of a coverage decision made by Medicare or their healthcare provider if they disagree with it.

• Patient Education: Medicare recipients have a right to be informed about their responsibilities and rights as beneficiaries. This includes information on how to access care, file complaints, and understand the Medicare program.

It's essential to note that while Medicare provides certain rights and protections to its beneficiaries, it's equally important for individuals to actively engage in their own care, express their preferences, and cooperate with their healthcare providers in decision-making.

These rights and principles are designed to uphold patient autonomy, respect for individual preferences, and a patient-centric healthcare model. Upholding the right of Medicare recipients to contribute to healthcare decisions empowers them to take greater control over their health and wellbeing.

9. Right to Understand Medicare Costs

The Right to Understand Medicare Costs is a fundamental component of the rights granted to Medicare recipients, aimed at promoting transparency and clarity in healthcare expenditures.

Under this right, Medicare recipients are entitled to the following:

• Comprehensive Cost Explanation: Medicare recipients have the right to receive a detailed cost breakdown of their medical care. This includes understanding the costs associated with any relevant services, tests, treatments, and medical procedures.

● Itemized Statements: Medicare recipients have the right to receive itemized statements detailing the costs of all services and procedures they undergo. These statements should include a cost breakdown, along with the price of any necessary medications, supplies, and other expenses.

● Advance Cost Notice: Medicare recipients have the right to receive prior notification of the expected costs of upcoming medical services. This allows recipients to make informed healthcare decisions and explore alternative options if necessary.

● Coverage Explanation: Medicare recipients have the right to understand how their insurance policies apply to certain services or treatments. This includes knowing which services are covered, any limitations or exclusions, and the charges or cost-sharing responsibilities.

● Accessible Information: Medicare recipients have the right to easily understandable information about Medicare costs. This includes providing information in a language they comprehend, in formats accessible to individuals with disabilities, and in a culturally sensitive manner, if applicable.

● Appeals and Complaints: Medicare recipients have the option to appeal a coverage decision or lodge a complaint if they believe their charges were made in error. This ensures that recipients can address any issues or discrepancies they encounter regarding their Medicare costs.

To empower Medicare recipients to make informed healthcare decisions, they must exercise their right to understand Medicare costs. This can aid them in comparing prices among healthcare providers, comprehending the costs of their medical services, and managing their healthcare expenditures more effectively.

Medicare providers and facilities are required to adhere to regulations that promote transparency, accurate billing procedures, and clear communication with Medicare recipients to ensure compliance with this right. To ensure they understand and can validate the costs associated with their care, Medicare recipients should actively engage in asking questions, seeking clarification, and reviewing their Medicare statements.

It's worth noting that Medicare recipients may also have access to resources such as Medicare Summary Notices (MSNs) and online tools provided by Medicare. These tools offer additional information on their healthcare expenses and services, further supporting the right to understand Medicare costs.

10. Right to File Complaints

A vital aspect of safeguarding the rights and interests of Medicare beneficiaries involves the capacity to lodge complaints. Medicare beneficiaries have the opportunity to address issues related to the quality of care, service accessibility, billing problems, and concerns about healthcare providers by filing a complaint. This not only enhances the overall standard of the Medicare program but also empowers beneficiaries to advocate for themselves.

Medicare beneficiaries can follow a specific process to lodge complaints. Often, the initial step involves directly communicating with the healthcare facility or professional to discuss the issue and seek an informal resolution.

If the problem remains unresolved, beneficiaries can reach out to their state's Beneficiary and Family Centered Care-Quality Improvement Organization (BFCC-QIO), which handles Medicare quality of care complaints. These organizations can assist with dispute resolution and mediation.

Another resource available to Medicare beneficiaries is the Medicare Beneficiary Ombudsman, an unbiased representative affiliated with the Centers for Medicare & Medicaid Services (CMS). The ombudsman can provide guidance, support, and help in resolving complaints.

In cases where informal resolution attempts are unsuccessful, beneficiaries can file a formal complaint with the relevant regulatory authority, such as CMS or their state health department.

Medicare beneficiaries can lodge complaints without fear of repercussions. It is unlawful for healthcare providers or facilities to retaliate against beneficiaries who exercise their rights to voice concerns or file complaints.

The Medicare program places a high priority on beneficiaries' complaints as a means to voice grievances, protect legal rights, and enhance healthcare services, thereby ensuring beneficiary well-being and satisfaction.

CHAPTER 9: HOW TO BUY MEDICARE INSURANCE BY YOURSELF

Greetings, Medicare DIY enthusiast! This section is tailored just for you. As a Medicare consumer, you appreciate the value of thorough research and informed decision-making. You are wary of sales pitches and prefer a hands-on approach to everything. Does this resonate with you? If you prefer bypassing a Medicare insurance agent, are prepared to invest a bit more time, and are comfortable navigating this process independently online, then you're in the right place!

Like the three paths of Medicare, there are three DIY options at your disposal. Each of these options can be applied to all three Medicare paths, but I suggest using different DIY options for each path.

Before proceeding, it's crucial to have a basic idea of the path you wish to pursue. Having completed the same checklists, you would have if you were working with a Medicare insurance agent can be immensely helpful. We've all experienced the rabbit hole of online research, losing hours without realizing where the time went or what we've achieved. As I've mentioned before, online marketers are adept at enticing you to click their ads and links, with the ultimate goal of getting you to call them or click something. Resist this urge. Keep your checklist(s) handy and adhere to the DIY guide below.

Bear in mind, these steps are subject to change. I will update these steps on the website as needed, but even if they alter slightly, you should still be able to reach your intended destination.

MEDICARE.GOV

Medicare.gov is the go-to website for individuals seeking information on Medicare coverage. As a government website, it offers unbiased information, free from sales pitches and flashy marketing. It presents all available options, allowing you to explore and research at your own pace without any pressure.

However, as discussed in Chapter Three, this website has several "Frustrating Flaws". While it does list all product options and allows you to enroll in Medicare Advantage and Medicare Part D Prescription Drug Plans, the Medicare Supplement section leaves much to be desired. The overall website navigation is cumbersome. While entering your location, prescriptions, and preferred pharmacies is straightforward, it falls short when searching for doctors under Medicare Advantage plans. Medicare.gov doesn't even host Medicare Advantage network data; you have to visit different websites for that. Additionally, the data sorting and filtering parameters are not user-friendly. In a nutshell, it's a government website that is outperformed by numerous Medicare insurance company and insurance agency websites.

This doesn't mean you should disregard it. On the contrary, it can be useful for two specific purposes: purchasing a Medicare Part D Prescription Drug Plan and narrowing down your Medicare Advantage options.

Option 1: **Bare-with-Medicare**

I highly suggest using Medicare.gov as your sole platform for purchasing your Medicare Part D Prescription Drug Plan. Medicare.gov offers a user-friendly and efficient platform for this purpose, likely surpassing the experience of working with a Medicare insurance agent. If you have your necessary documents and checklists prepared, the process can be completed in less than an hour.

To clarify, by choosing this route, you will be utilizing Original Medicare for your healthcare coverage and purchasing a separate Medicare Part D Prescription Drug Plan. The process of acquiring a Medicare Part D Prescription Drug Plan through Medicare.gov is straightforward.

Here's a step-by-step guide:

1. Access Medicare.gov on your web browser.

2. Select "Find Health and Drug Plans."

   - Although you can create or log into an account, it's not a requirement.

3. When prompted, enter your ZIP code. From the dropdown menu, select "Drug Plan (Part D)" and click "Start."

4. Choose the last option, "I don't get help from any of these programs," then proceed to the next step.

5. When asked, "Do you want to see your drug costs when you compare plans?", select yes.

6. In the "Add prescription drug" section, input all of your prescriptions, including dosages and frequency. Refer to your worksheet if you have one.

7. After entering all your prescriptions, click "Done Adding Drugs."

8. The next page prompts you to identify your pharmacy. Search for your preferred pharmacy by name or use the map provided. You can list up to five pharmacies, but most likely, you'll only need one. Click "Done" once you've finished entering data.

The resulting page will display all your Medicare Part D Prescription Drug Plan options. By default, the results are sorted by "Lowest Drug + Premium Cost," which is a practical way to organize your options. If you prefer plans without deductibles, you can filter the results by selecting "Lowest yearly drug deductible." If you want to sort by the lowest monthly premium, you have that option as well.

Regardless of the sorting method you choose, focus on the top three results. Quickly review each plan to ensure it has a rating of three and a half stars or above. Avoid considering any plan rated under three stars. If a plan is flagged as "Plan too new to be measured," it's acceptable, but note that it's a newly introduced Medicare Part D Prescription Drug Plan.

The subsequent step can be as simple or complex as you prefer. You can compare up to three Medicare Part D Prescription Drug Plans side-by-side or simply choose the top result.

When ready to enroll, click "Enroll." This will lead you to a page where you'll confirm your enrollment period. If you need a reminder, refer to your checklist or workbook, or revisit Chapter Two to ensure you're using the correct enrollment period.

Once you've selected your enrollment period, click "Next."

This initiates a seven-step process:

1. Enter your Medicare number, found on your red, white, and blue Medicare card. Acknowledge that you've read and understood the contents of the page, and click Next.

2. Fill out your name, date of birth, gender, and phone number. Ensure your name matches what's on your Medicare card. Click Next.

3. Enter your primary home address. Click Next.

4. The next section inquiries about any other drug coverage you have, your employment status, and your preference for receiving Medicare insurance plan documents. Once completed, click Next.

5. This section asks if you'd like the monthly premiums deducted from your Social Security or Railroad Retirement Board (RRB) benefits. You can choose this option or opt to pay your plan directly. Be aware that it may take several months for Medicare, the Medicare insurance company, and Social Security to synchronize billing. If you'd rather avoid this potential inconvenience, select Auto Bill Pay.

6. This section contains legal language asking you to confirm your previous entries. Complete it and click Next.

7. This is the confirmation screen.

Congratulations! You've successfully enrolled in a Medicare Part D Prescription Drug Plan.

WHAT'S NEXT?

You should receive your Medicare Part D Prescription Drug Plan card via mail within approximately two weeks. You'll also receive additional information through mail unless you chose to receive plan documents via email. If there are any issues with your application, the Medicare insurance company will contact you. It's crucial that you respond promptly.

Option 2: Original Medicare + Medicare Part D Prescription Drug Plan + Medicare Supplement

I would suggest utilizing Medicare.gov as your sole platform for purchasing your Medicare Part D Prescription Drug Plan, and then resorting to a Hybrid Agency website for your Medicare Supplement plan.

Just a quick recap: this option implies that you're using Original Medicare for your medical healthcare coverage, supplementing it with a Medicare Supplement plan, and purchasing a Medicare Part D Prescription Drug Plan. This process is divided into two steps.

Step 1: Implement the DIY method previously detailed to purchase your Medicare Part D Prescription Drug Plan.

Step 2: Employ an online Hybrid Agency to acquire your Medicare Supplement plan.

You have the option to purchase a Medicare Supplement plan from any of the Hybrid Agencies. However, at the time of writing this, many of these websites only allow you to delve a step or two into the research before requesting more personal information or urging you to dial their toll-free number.

I'm not endorsing any specific Hybrid Agency. However, it's impossible for me to guide you through more than one website experience while keeping this chapter concise. Feel free to choose any hybrid agency that suits you — I have no preference. Each one employs a similar process to what I've described below, with minor variations. Many hybrid agencies ask for your email address and phone number upfront, but some do not. I prefer not to provide my email or phone number unless necessary, as I prefer not to receive calls or emails. However, I may be overly cautious.

Regardless of the hybrid agency you choose, ensure you're in their Medicare Supplement section, not their Medicare Advantage or Medicare Part D Prescription Drug Plan section.

Why do I advocate using a hybrid agency website for this? Firstly, I've already explained in Chapter Three why Medicare.gov is practically ineffective for Medicare Supplement research and enrollment. Another reason is that it spares you the trouble of visiting each Medicare Supplement insurance company's website individually. Hybrid agency websites rank, sort, and filter these for you. Most, if not all, of these hybrid agency websites feature large Medicare Supplement companies on their platforms. Many hybrid agencies also list numerous smaller, lesser-known Medicare Supplement insurance companies, should you wish to explore those. Lastly, even though you're purchasing this in a

DIY style online, you're still transacting through an insurance agency. This means you might receive communications and outreach from the agency.

WHAT'S NEXT?

You'll receive confirmation letters or emails acknowledging your application. If they need to verify any information you provided on the application, the insurance company will also give you a follow-up call.

Expect to receive your ID cards in the mail within two weeks. Since you purchased the policy through a hybrid agency, you may also receive subsequent correspondence from the agency.

There's a second DIY option for this — purchasing your Medicare Part D Prescription Drug Plan on Medicare.gov and then buying your Medicare Supplement plan directly from the Medicare insurance companies. The major players in Medicare Supplement insurance include Mutual of Omaha, Humana, United Healthcare (AARP co-branded), CVS Health/Aetna, and various Blue Cross and Blue Shield plans. The only drawback with this approach is that you will need to visit each of their websites to individually compare prices and plans. While it's doable, it will consume a significant amount of your time. Considering the time investment, you might be better off setting aside your DIY tendencies and simply contacting an independent Medicare insurance agent.

Option 3: **Medicare Advantage (MAPD)**

When it comes to purchasing a Medicare Advantage plan, you have two self-guided options. The first involves utilizing Medicare.gov to narrow down your top three preferences, then transitioning to the Medicare insurance company's websites to finalize your research and purchase the policy. The second option is to use a hybrid agency website to acquire your Medicare Advantage plan.

Remember, if you opt for this route, you're selecting a Medicare Advantage plan that incorporates Medicare Part D benefits, also known as an MAPD plan, which provides both medical and prescription drug coverage.

OPTION 3: VERSION 1

Medicare.gov + Medicare insurance company websites.

This version requires navigating through multiple websites before making your final purchase. It's advisable to have your checklists (available on the Prepare for Medicare website) completed and at your disposal. If not, ensure you have your prescription drugs and doctors' details readily available.

This process is quite comprehensive and labor-intensive, potentially taking one to two hours to complete. This is due to a limitation on the Medicare.gov website, which doesn't allow you to check which providers are in or out of the network. Hence, we'll use Medicare.gov to narrow down your options, then switch to the Medicare insurance company's website to check for doctors and enroll. Let's get started!

Here's a step-by-step guide:

1. Open Medicare.gov in your web browser.

2. Select "Find Health and Drug Plans."

3. Input your ZIP code, choose a Plan Type from the dropdown menu, and select Medicare Advantage Plan. Click "Start."

4. Answer the question, "Do you get help with your costs from one of these programs?" by selecting "I don't get help from any of these programs."

5. When asked, "Do you want to see your drug costs when you compare plans?" click yes.

6. In the "Add prescription drugs" section, input all your prescriptions, including dosages and frequency.

7. Once you've added all your prescriptions, click "Done Adding Drugs."

8. The next screen prompts you to find your Pharmacy. Search for yours by name, or use the map provided on the page. You can enter up to five, but most likely, you only use one.

The Medicare Advantage plans available in your area will be displayed, sorted by "Lowest drug + Premium cost."

Before proceeding, let's revisit the considerations I recommended earlier in the book for purchasing a Medicare Advantage plan, listed from most to least important:

1. Are your doctors and preferred hospital in the insurance company's provider network? If unsure, call their offices to confirm.

2. Monthly premium—the lower, the better, but don't be swayed by a $0 plan premium automatically.

3. Primary care and specialist doctor copays—the lower, the better.

4. Prescription drug coverage—Are all your prescription drugs on the formulary, i.e., are they covered?

5. Where do your prescription drugs fall within the formulary? Tier 1 drugs are the least expensive, while Tier 4+ are the most expensive.

6. Prescription drug copays—the lower, the better.

7. Avoid deductibles on prescription drug coverage.

8. MOOP—try to keep it under $4,000 per year.

9. Avoid deductibles on medical coverage.

10. Inpatient hospitalization coverage—the lowest daily copays for the fewest number of days is the best.

11. Outpatient costs—try to find coverage at a fixed-dollar amount; avoid coinsurance if possible.

12. Diagnostic procedure costs—try to find coverage at a fixed-dollar amount; avoid coinsurance if possible.

13. "Extra" benefits (dental, vision, hearing, etc.). Dental allowance should be at least $1,000 per year.

14. Star rating—needs to be 3.5 or higher.

Now, with the default screen displaying all the Medicare Advantage plans available in your area (sorted by Lowest drug + Premium cost), it's time to use this list in conjunction with the filter and sort options on Medicare.gov.

FILTERING

Begin by navigating to the filter feature, situated in the top right corner of your screen. This will prompt a pop-up window to appear. Within this window, locate and click on the drop-down menu labeled "Drug Coverage Options", ensuring you select "Includes Drug Coverage". If you have a preference for either PPO or HMO plans, you can refine your search results by selecting the appropriate option. If you have no preference, select both.

While in the Filter section, select Star Ratings and choose "3 stars and up". Feel free to explore other filtering options that align with your preferences. Once satisfied, click the "Apply" button. This will close the pop-up window and display your filtered plan options.

Now, examine your results. You can rearrange the order of your results (the default setting is Lowest drug + premium cost) by utilizing the drop-down menu in the top right corner. Here, you have four sorting options: "Lowest yearly drug deductible", "Lowest health plan deductible", "Lowest monthly premium", and "Lowest drug + premium cost".

SORTING

Start by sorting your results by "Lowest monthly premium". The first Medicare Advantage plan that appears will display the premium, an estimated annual cost of your drug and premium, the health deductible, and the drug deductible, as well as the Maximum Out-of-Pocket (MOOP) amount.

Towards the bottom of the page, you'll find a button labeled "Add to compare". Use this to select your preferred plans. Aim to find a plan with the lowest monthly premium, no medical or prescription drug deductibles, and a MOOP of $4,000 or less. If such a plan is not available, choose the one with the lowest MOOP and deductible amounts from a familiar brand. Click "Add to compare". Repeat this process for two more plans, totaling three.

Once you've made your selections, they will appear at the bottom of the page. When you're ready, click the "Compare" button. This will generate a side-by-side comparison of your chosen plans.

Now, it's your turn to scrutinize the details of each plan, aligning them with the recommendations provided above.

The next step involves some legwork on your part due to Medicare.gov's inability to list in-network providers on their website. Before proceeding to enrollment, it's crucial to ensure your preferred doctors are included in the network. To do this, select the first plan you're interested in and click "Plan Details".

Scroll down to the bottom of the new webpage that appears. Here, you'll find a hyperlink labeled "View Plan website". Clicking this will open a new tab redirecting you to the Medicare insurance company's website. Locate the "Find a Doctor" link on their webpage.

For example, if you were researching a Humana plan, you'd land on www.humana.com/medicare. Once there, find the "Find a Doctor" or "Find a Provider" option. Then, search for your doctors, hospitals, or other healthcare providers. Ensure all your preferred healthcare providers are listed in the network.

Once you've confirmed your doctors are included in your chosen plan, return to the Medicare.gov page. Scroll back to the top of the page and click "Go back to plan comparison". This will bring you back to your selected plans.

Repeat this process for all your chosen plans. Once you've identified the plans that include your doctors, click "Enroll".

When you're ready to enroll, have the following information on hand:

• Your Medicare number (found on your red, white, and blue Medicare card).

• Information about any other health coverage you have, including policy and group numbers (found on your health insurance card).

• Dates of any recent changes, such as moving to a new address.

While this process is quite extensive and involves several steps, it's a key reason why many individuals opt to purchase a Medicare Advantage plan with the help of a Medicare insurance agent.

OPTION 3: REVISED VERSION

Utilizing Hybrid Agency Websites

This alternative involves employing a hybrid agency website to investigate, study, and register for a Medicare Advantage plan. Ensure you have your checklists at hand to serve as reference guides. At a minimum, you'll need your prescription drugs and doctors' lists readily available.

Why do I suggest using a hybrid agency website for this? I've previously explained why Medicare.gov isn't an ideal platform for purchasing a Medicare Advantage plan independently, but it essentially boils down to this: Medicare.gov lacks the ability to search for in-network doctors. A hybrid agency eliminates the inconvenience of the DIY Option #3, Version 1. It eliminates the need to use Medicare.gov and sift through each individual Medicare insurance company's website. It's simply more efficient and quicker. Hybrid agency websites rank, classify, and filter all your Medicare Advantage options, and allow you to search for your providers all in one place.

The steps for this method are fewer than the previous option, Version 1, and should take approximately an hour. A note of caution: because this is essentially an online insurance agency, each agency must have a contract with Medicare Advantage insurance companies to display and sell their plans on their websites. This means that, unlike Medicare.gov, they may not display all the Medicare Advantage plans available in your region. This is particularly true in large metropolitan areas, which usually have many smaller or regional Medicare Advantage plans available, but for whatever reason, the hybrid agency doesn't have a contract with them to sell their Medicare Advantage plans. Lastly, even though you're purchasing this independently online, you're still acquiring it through an insurance agency. This means you may receive communications and outreach from the agency. Ready? Let's get started!

Essentially, you need to ensure you're on their Medicare Advantage section, not their life insurance, car insurance, Medicare Supplement, or Medicare Part D Prescription Drug Plan sections. If you enter the address as I've provided it in the back of the book, it should direct you straight to the Medicare section.

WHAT'S NEXT?

If you've successfully followed the steps and registered for a Medicare Advantage plan, congratulations! You've completed the process! Well, almost. If everything has been done correctly, you can anticipate receiving your ID cards and other plan documents in the mail. If there was an error on the application, expect the insurance agency to contact you. Or the Medicare insurance company may reach out to you.

Purchasing a Medicare Part D Prescription Drug Plan on Medicare.gov independently is relatively straightforward. (It's the simplest the DIY approach gets.) Buying a Medicare Supplement online is likely the next simplest due to fewer offerings. Purchasing a Medicare Advantage plan becomes exceedingly complex and challenging without expert guidance.

If you decide to go the DIY route, fantastic! However, be aware that the majority of people eventually seek professional assistance in making this decision and enrolling in Medicare insurance plans. If you're feeling overwhelmed or uncertain, consulting a seasoned Medicare insurance professional is likely the best course of action and one I strongly recommend you consider.

CONCLUSION

Reflecting on the insights gained and their impact is essential as we conclude this enlightening journey through the Medicare landscape. The wisdom acquired from each section equips you to adeptly navigate the intricate world of Medicare. Remember, you hold the reins to your healthcare choices, and by understanding the workings of Medicare, you can make choices that not only protect your health but also facilitate financial savings.

However, our exploration doesn't end here. We delve into "Strategies for Enhanced Health after 65" in this concluding segment. We offer an additional chapter brimming with valuable tips and strategies to maintain your health and wellbeing beyond the boundaries of Medicare coverage as you embark on this fresh phase of life. You're merely at the beginning of your journey towards a healthier, more secure future, and we're honored to serve as your trustworthy companion throughout this book.

So, harness the strength of knowledge, the benefits of Medicare, and the tranquility derived from being well-informed. Let this book be your compass as you traverse the complex terrain of Medicare, ensuring a brighter, healthier future for you and your dear ones. It's time to delve into the intricacies of your healthcare plan and seize unparalleled control of your health.

Made in the USA
Las Vegas, NV
04 March 2024